GATTEGNO MATHEMATICS

TEXT-BOOK 4

The Text-book Series

1. Qualitative arithmetic.
   The study of numbers from 1 to 20.

2. Study of numbers up to 1000.
   The four operations.

3. Applied arithmetic.

4. Fractions, Decimals, Percentages.

5. Study of numbers.

6. Applied mathematics.

7. Algebra and geometry.

GATTEGNO

MATHEMATICS

TEXT-BOOK 4

by

C. GATTEGNO

EDUCATIONAL SOLUTIONS
NEW YORK, N.Y. 10003

The title GATTEGNO MATHEMATICS
embodies an approach best expressed by
the phrase The Subordination of Teaching
to Learning. The programme covered in
this series envisages the use of colored
rods (ALGEBRICKS) and other books
and printed materials that are obtainable
from:

EDUCATIONAL SOLUTIONS INC.

821 Broadway, New York, N.Y. 10003

Printed in Great Britain by
Lamport Gilbert Printers Ltd.,
Wantage Road, Reading, England

CONTENTS

I

FRACTIONS AS OPERATORS

Part I

FRACTIONS AS OPERATORS

Operators

1. If we start with a red rod and ask for its *double* we get another rod, a pink one. So the word 'double' when heard makes us do something. For that reason we call such a word an operator.

So an operator is a sign which prompts us to do something.

Double is an operator, treble is another, double double is yet another, and so on.

If we say, 'Give me six of these objects', six will be used as an operator. So in 6×3, or six threes, six is an operator and 3 a kind of thing, of which six are required.

Let us agree, as we have done until now, that we write and read operations on numbers from left to right, as we read ordinary writing. Then in each multiplication the first numeral will be an operator, the rest of the product a thing.

Underline the operators in:

$$4 \times 3 \qquad 3 \times 4 \qquad 4 \times 5 \times 2 \qquad 15 \times 3 \times 4$$

Inverse operators

2. Just as we say six of . . . , we are used to saying half of . . . . Half is, therefore, an operator. Indeed, if we ask for half of something, an action must follow to produce the result. For example, if we ask for a rod which is half of the red rod, we get a white rod.

We have already learnt to associate half with double, third with treble, and so on.

When we wrote $r=2w$ or $g=3w$, we also read the relationship in reverse and said w is half of r and wrote $w=\frac{1}{2} \times r$; w is one third of g and wrote $w=\frac{1}{3} \times g$. The operators double

3

and half, treble and third, and so on or $2\times$ and $\frac{1}{2}\times$; $3\times$ and $\frac{1}{3}\times$ form pairs of what we shall call **inverse operators**.

Give the inverse operators of:

$\frac{1}{7}\times$ $\qquad\qquad$ $5\times$ $\qquad\qquad$ $8\times$

$10\times$ $\qquad\qquad$ $\frac{1}{9}\times$ $\qquad\qquad$ $\frac{1}{6}\times$

Write your own examples.

Composition of operators

3. Just as we can say double double, we could say half half and ask, say, for half half the pink rod and get a rod.

Can you get an answer to the request of:

$\qquad\qquad$ double the treble of . . .

$\quad$ or $\quad$ treble the double of . . .

$\quad$ or $\quad$ treble the treble of . . .

$\quad$ or $\quad$ double the double of the treble of . . .

$\quad$ or $\quad$ double the double of the double of the double of . . .

Each time give yourself a rod or a number.

Can you find the inverse operator of the operators above?

You already know that half of half of is written $\frac{1}{2}\times\frac{1}{2}\times$

Read $\quad$ $\frac{1}{2}\times\frac{1}{3}\times$ $\qquad\qquad$ $\frac{1}{3}\times\frac{1}{2}\times$ $\qquad\qquad$ $\frac{1}{5}\times\frac{1}{4}\times$

And find the answer to

$\qquad$ $\frac{1}{2}\times\frac{1}{3}\times24$ $\qquad$ $\frac{1}{3}\times\frac{1}{2}\times12$ $\qquad$ $\frac{1}{5}\times\frac{1}{4}\times40$

Find operators like the ones above that would change:

$\qquad\qquad$ 96 into 12 $\qquad\qquad$ 84 into 14

$\qquad\qquad$ 81 into 9 $\qquad\qquad\;$ 5 into 90

4. Operators can be combined in any numbers. You already know that

$\qquad$ $\frac{1}{2}\times84=42$ $\qquad$ $\frac{1}{2}\times42=21$ $\qquad$ $\frac{1}{3}\times21=7$

or $\frac{1}{7}\times21=3$. So you can see that

$\qquad$ $\frac{1}{2}\times(\frac{1}{2}\times84)=21$ $\qquad\qquad$ $\frac{1}{3}\times(\frac{1}{2}\times(\frac{1}{2}\times84))=7$

$\qquad\qquad\qquad$ $\frac{1}{7}\times(\frac{1}{2}\times(\frac{1}{2}\times84))=3$

4

All of these can be written without the brackets as:

$\frac{1}{2} \times \frac{1}{2} \times 84$ $\qquad$ $\frac{1}{3} \times \frac{1}{3} \times \frac{1}{2} \times 84$ $\qquad$ $\frac{1}{7} \times \frac{1}{2} \times \frac{1}{2} \times 84$

Find

$\frac{1}{2} \times \frac{1}{2} \times \frac{1}{2} \times 48 =$ $\qquad$ $\frac{1}{3} \times \frac{1}{3} \times 27 =$ $\qquad$ $\frac{1}{3} \times \frac{1}{3} \times \frac{1}{3} \times 81 =$

$\frac{1}{5} \times \frac{1}{2} \times \frac{1}{2} \times 100 =$ $\qquad$ $\frac{1}{5} \times \frac{1}{5} \times 75 =$ $\qquad$ $\frac{1}{3} \times \frac{1}{5} \times 45 =$

$\frac{1}{2} \times \frac{1}{2} \times \frac{1}{2} \times \frac{1}{2} \times \frac{1}{2} \times 128 =$ $\qquad$ $\frac{1}{2} \times \frac{1}{3} \times \frac{1}{4} \times \frac{1}{5} \times 240 =$

Equivalent operators

5. You already know that $\frac{1}{2} \times 12$ and $\frac{2}{4} \times 12$ and $\frac{3}{6} \times 12$ and $\frac{6}{12} \times 12$ give the same answer 6.

Since the length on which you operate (12) and the answer you obtain (6) are respectively equal in all cases, but since the operators do not look the same ($\frac{1}{2}$, $\frac{2}{4}$, $\frac{3}{6}$, $\frac{6}{12}$), we shall use the word equivalent to tell that they have the same effect but are not the same themselves, and we shall write:

$$\frac{1}{2} = \frac{2}{4} = \frac{3}{6} = \frac{6}{12}$$

reading the sign $=$ as equivalent.

Had we started with 24, we would have found that:

$\frac{1}{2} \times 24 = 12$ $\qquad$ $\frac{2}{4} \times 24 = 12$ $\qquad$ $\frac{3}{6} \times 24 = 12$

$\frac{4}{8} \times 24 = 12$ $\qquad$ $\frac{6}{12} \times 24 = 12$ $\qquad$ $\frac{12}{24} \times 24 = 12$

which would add two fractions to the equivalences given above, or:

$$\frac{1}{2} = \frac{2}{4} = \frac{3}{6} = \frac{4}{8} = \frac{6}{12} = \frac{12}{24}$$

Can we add new operators to these equivalences by again changing the number we work on?

Do it with 10, 14, 18, and so on.

Since each new number will add at least one operator and since we can always find a number larger than those we already have, we shall write our **sequence of equivalences** as follows

$$\frac{1}{2} = \frac{2}{4} = \frac{3}{6} = \frac{4}{8} = \frac{5}{10} = \frac{6}{12} = \ldots$$

where the dots at the end tell us that we could go on and on finding new operators.

5

6. Had we started with $\frac{1}{3} \times 24$ or $\frac{1}{3} \times 18$ or $\frac{1}{3} \times 36$ which equivalent fractions would we have found?

Write them down and try to find how to write all the operators equivalent to $\frac{1}{3}$, as we did above for $\frac{1}{2}$.

We shall from now on talk of **family of equivalence** every time we think of **all** the operators that are equivalent to each other. Naturally, we can only write the first few and simply think of the others.

To help you think of the whole family, the following is useful. You already know that each number has as many equivalent expressions as you wish. Of these, some can be written more easily than others. For example:

$5 = \frac{1}{2} \times 10 = \frac{1}{4} \times 20 = \frac{1}{5} \times 25 = \frac{1}{7} \times 35$ and so on, are each

easier than $\frac{1}{10} \times 30 + \frac{1}{5} \times 10$

From each of the above we can get another equivalent expression if we write:

$5 = \frac{1}{2} \times 2 \times 5 = \frac{1}{4} \times 4 \times 5 = \frac{1}{5} \times 5 \times 5 = \frac{1}{7} \times 7 \times 5$ etc.

or new ones if we write

$$5 = \frac{2 \times 5}{2} = \frac{4 \times 5}{4} = \frac{5 \times 5}{5} = \frac{7 \times 5}{7} \text{ etc.}$$

or, by taking the inverse operators for each, we get:

$$\frac{1}{5} = \frac{2}{2 \times 5} = \frac{4}{4 \times 5} = \frac{5}{5 \times 5} = \frac{7}{7 \times 5} \text{ etc.}$$

which we can write as:

$$\frac{1}{5} = \frac{2 \times 1}{2 \times 5} = \frac{4 \times 1}{4 \times 5} = \frac{5 \times 1}{5 \times 5} = \frac{7 \times 1}{7 \times 5} \text{ etc.}$$

If we compare $\dfrac{3 \times 1}{3 \times 5}$ with $\dfrac{2 \times 1}{2 \times 5}$ we find that they are equiva-

lent because each is equivalent to $\frac{1}{5}$, so we could insert $\dfrac{3 \times 1}{3 \times 5}$

6

between $\dfrac{2\times1}{2\times5}$ and $\dfrac{4\times1}{4\times5}$, and $\dfrac{6\times1}{6\times5}$ between the last two

written above. Now we have the following:

$$\frac{1}{5}=\frac{2\times1}{2\times5}=\frac{3\times1}{3\times5}=\frac{4\times1}{4\times5}=\frac{5\times1}{5\times5}=\frac{6\times1}{6\times5}=\frac{7\times1}{7\times5}=$$

Can you write the next few?

Is $\dfrac{121\times1}{121\times5}$ a member of this family? and $\dfrac{724,569\times1}{724,569\times5}$?

How do you know?

Can you say when a fraction will belong to the family above? and to the family whose first member is $\frac{1}{2}$? or $\frac{1}{3}$?

7. In Part II we shall study all these questions again but there we shall be looking sometimes at the pair of rods or the pair of numbers and sometimes at the operator relating them. You will need to know this: that every time an operator is written down or talked about, you may think of any number of operators equivalent to it, forming a family of equivalence. $\frac{1}{2}$ or $\frac{1}{3}$ or $\frac{1}{4}$ are short ways of saying that we think of all the equivalent expressions of the type met above, though *you* may know of many others besides. This you have already practised very often when you have thought that, for example, 2 had any number of equivalent expressions but that not all of these were needed if the expression $1+1$ was the one which helped you find the answer to a problem.

II

STUDY OF FRACTIONS

PART II

STUDY OF FRACTIONS

Ordered pairs

1. What is the white rod of the red rod? and the red of the pink? and the light green of the dark green? and the pink of the tan? and the yellow of the orange?

Because we measure the small rod by the big one, we get answers that are all equal. So it would also be if we measured the big one by the small one.

If we make a length by putting rods end to end and if we then make another twice this length, the pair formed with these two lengths can be looked at in two ways: measuring by the small one we can say the big one is its double. Measuring by the big one the other is its half.

In order to make our writing easy we shall use brackets and two figures or letters separated by a comma, to represent the pair we are considering. (l,L) is a pair of lengths, and *we shall always write the measuring length second.*

Thus (2,4) and (4,2) are the two pairs formed by the red and pink rods. The first says the pink measures the red, and $(2,4)=\frac{1}{2}$ and the second that the red measures the pink and $(4,2)=\frac{2}{1}$.

Fractions can now be written either as **ordered pairs** in brackets or as two numbers separated by a bar.

Write as ordered pairs:

$$\tfrac{1}{3} \quad \tfrac{2}{8} \quad \tfrac{3}{2} \quad \tfrac{1}{7} \quad \tfrac{3}{8} \quad \tfrac{5}{17} \quad \tfrac{12}{7} \quad \tfrac{21}{5} \quad \tfrac{27}{8} \quad \tfrac{14}{15} \quad \tfrac{99}{19} \quad \tfrac{33}{12} \quad \tfrac{41}{57} \quad \tfrac{62}{63}$$

Write as fractions the following ordered pairs:

(1,2), (2,1), (3,7), (8,3), (7,12), (8,27), (27,5), (14,15) (62,67).

Family of equivalent ordered pairs

2. Write the pairs named by their colors at the beginning of No. 1 as fractions and as ordered pairs.

10

Take the white and light green rods and form the pairs they can give. Can you find other pairs that give the same fractions?

Do the same with white and pink, and white and yellow rods.

From the pairs you form give the fractions.

When ordered pairs give the same fraction we shall call them **equivalent**. This means that they are of equal value.

Thus $(1,2), (2,4), (3,6), (4,8), (5,10)$ are all equal or equivalent to $\frac{1}{2}$.

We shall write in two ways:

either $\frac{1}{2}=\frac{2}{4}=\frac{3}{6}=\frac{4}{8}=\frac{5}{10}=\ \ldots$

or $(1,2)=(2,4)=(3,6)=(4,8)=(5,10)=\ \ldots$

Can you write the first few terms of the **family of pairs** equivalent to

$\frac{1}{3}=$

$\frac{2}{3}=$

$\frac{1}{4}=$

$\frac{3}{4}=$

$\frac{1}{5}=$

$\frac{2}{9}=$

Use your rods when you cannot, and also to check your answers.

First element of a family of equivalence

3. If an ordered pair is given, can you find another equivalent to it whose numbers are smaller than in the given pair? Try the following:

$(5,10)=$

$(6,18)=$

$(15,25)=$

One way of doing this is to make the two lengths and find whether there is one rod that goes exactly into both lengths, noting the number of times it goes into each. Thus for $(14,21)$ both lengths can be made with black rods which go twice into the first length and three times into the other. Hence $(14,21)=(2\times7,\ 3\times7)=(2,3)$.

11

This last method gives at once the pair with the smallest numbers or, as we shall say, the smallest terms. This pair is the first in the family. Sometimes we shall call it the **irreducible pair**, because we cannot make its terms any smaller.

If we had started with (28,42), we should have found that we could have made these lengths with red rods, since the two terms are even, or with black rods; so we can find the irreducible pair in these three ways:

$$(28,42)=(14\times2,\ 21\times2)=(14,21)=(2\times7,\ 3\times7)=(2,3)$$

$$(28,42)=(4\times7,\ 6\times7)=(4,6)=(2,3)$$

$$(28,42)=(2\times14,\ 3\times14)=(2,3)$$

Writing the first line as fractions we have:

$$\frac{28}{42}=\frac{14\times2}{21\times2}=\frac{14}{21}=\frac{2\times7}{3\times7}=\frac{2}{3}$$

In No. 2 we formed families of equivalent fractions, or ordered pairs, starting with the irreducible ones. Here we have started with any one fraction and found to which family it belongs by finding the irreducible pair to which it is equivalent.

Find the family to which each of the following fractions belongs:

(35,70)
(18,54)
(72,12)
(81,27)
(25,125)
(91,169)

Equivalent fractions

4. Every time we are given a fraction we know how to obtain others equivalent to it. Can you say in words how? If we write (a,b) for any ordered pair in which the length a is measured by the length b, can you say if the following are or are not equivalent to it?

12

$(3 \times a, 3 \times b)$	$(5 \times a, 5 \times b)$	$(7 \times a, 7 \times b)$
$(a, 2 \times b)$	$(5 \times a, b)$	$(5 \times a, 7 \times b)$
$\left(\frac{a}{2}, \frac{b}{2}\right)$	$\left(\frac{a}{3}, \frac{b}{3}\right)$	$\left(\frac{a}{7}, \frac{b}{7}\right)$
$\left(\frac{a}{3}, \frac{b}{5}\right)$	$\left(\frac{a}{5}, \frac{b}{7}\right)$	$\left(\frac{a}{9}, \frac{b}{11}\right)$

5. Write down a few fractions equivalent to the following:

(A,B) (A,C)

(B,A) (Z,T)

6. When we are given a fraction with figures instead of letters, is there an end to the family of fractions equivalent to it?

$\frac{2}{3}=$

$\frac{7}{8}=$

Will it be different if we do not say what the lengths are and write instead of $\frac{2}{3}$ and $\frac{7}{8}$, $\frac{a}{b}$ and $\frac{c}{d}$?

All you are asked is to note what you do when dealing with numbers and to do it again in cases where the numbers are not given.

Reciprocals

7. If (a,b) is a fraction, (b,a) is another fraction called its reciprocal.

Find the reciprocals of the following:

$(7,3)$	$(2,5)$	$(11,13)$
$(41,93)$	$(11,97)$	$(51,15)$

What is the reciprocal of the reciprocal of a fraction?

If we start with the following pairs

$(1,2)$ $(1,3)$ $(1,4)$ $(1,5)$ $(1,6)$

their reciprocals are:

$(2,1)$ $(3,1)$ $(4,1)$ $(5,1)$ $(6,1)$

What is the next step?

13

So far, in these text-books, we have used the signs 2, 3, 4 . . . to denote the number of times the white rod goes into the length of a bigger rod or of rods placed end to end. Accordingly, we have called the length of the orange and green rods end to end 13, because we used the white rod to measure that length. We can now see that we could equally well have written (13,1) or $\frac{13}{1}$ instead of 13, and this would have made it obvious that we were using 1 as the unit of measurement. So we see that *whole numbers are ordered pairs whose second term is 1 which is not written but is always understood.* When we meet (5,1) for instance, we can write $\frac{5}{1}$ or 5 as may best suit the operation we are carrying out.

Write the possible forms of the following:

(12,1)	$\frac{9}{1}$
(7,1)	(17,1)
72	$\frac{15}{1}$
$\frac{121}{1}$	83
(57,1)	(73,1)

Can you find the answers to:

$\frac{9}{1}+(13,1)+8=$ $\qquad$ $(11,1)+(17,1)+\frac{3}{1}-\frac{6}{1}-4=$

$(17,1)-(12,1)+\frac{9}{1}=$ $\qquad$ $7+(21,1)-\frac{1}{3}\times(15,1)=$

8.   The reciprocal of 13 is $\frac{1}{13}$ if we use the notation with the bar.

In this notation the reciprocal of the reciprocal of 13 can be written $\dfrac{1}{\frac{1}{13}}$, and we know this is 13.

Write the reciprocal of the reciprocal of the reciprocal of 13 using the bar notation, and find its value. Do it for 12, 121, 372.

If we go on taking reciprocals we only need to write more bars and more 1's. See if you can read:

$$\cfrac{1}{\cfrac{1}{\cfrac{1}{9}}} \qquad \cfrac{1}{\cfrac{1}{\cfrac{1}{21}}}$$

Start at the bottom.
Find the value of these fractions.

If we start with $\frac{2}{3}$, its reciprocal is $\frac{3}{2}$.

It can also be written using the above notation, $\dfrac{1}{\frac{2}{3}}$

The reciprocal of $\dfrac{1}{\frac{2}{3}}$ is $\dfrac{1}{\frac{1}{\frac{2}{3}}}$, and so on.

What is the fourth reciprocal of $\frac{5}{7}$?

What is the seventh reciprocal of $\frac{3}{4}$?

Do you see a way of knowing at once the value of any number of reciprocals of any fraction?

Addition of pairs

9.   If we write $12+13$ we know the answer is 25.

If we write $(12,1)+(13,1)$, what is the answer?

We can add ordered pairs of numbers when the second term in all of them is equal to 1.

The lengths of 12 and 13 can be measured by any other rod we choose and, if we add them, we shall measure the resultant length by that same chosen rod. If, for example, we choose the yellow rod, we shall write down our addition like this:

$(12,5)+(13,5)=(25,5)$

The sign $+$ means only that we add 12 and 13, which are the numbers measured by the yellow rod. 5 is left untouched because it is the unit of measurement. It therefore appears again in the answer.

Whenever we add fractions which have the same measuring unit we add what is measured and write down the answer, showing that the measuring unit has been kept unchanged.

Here are two examples written first as ordered pairs and then with the bar notation:

$(7,2)+(5,2)=(12,2)$ because $7+5=12$

$(15,3)+(17,3)=(32,3)$ because $15+17=32$.

$\frac{7}{2}+\frac{5}{2}=\frac{7+5}{2}=\frac{12}{2}$

$\frac{15}{3}+\frac{17}{3}=\frac{15+17}{3}=\frac{32}{3}$

15

Find the value of the following additions using the procedure above:

(2,13)+(4,13)+(9,13)= $\frac{2}{7}+\frac{11}{7}=$

(8,15)+(9,15)+(7,15)= $\frac{4}{9}+\frac{3}{9}+\frac{1}{9}=$

$\frac{1}{6}+\frac{2}{6}+\frac{3}{6}+\frac{4}{6}+\frac{5}{6}=$

(1,72)+(12,72)+(24,72)+(36,72)=

Subtraction of pairs

10. Can 6=10−4 also be written as (6,1)=(10,1)−(4,1)? Can we subtract pairs when the second term is the same in both but is not 1? Let us measure the dark green, the orange and the pink rod by the light green rod. We still have 6=10−4. This will be written this time: (6,3)=(10,3)−(4,3). So when we want to subtract two pairs having the same second term, it is enough to subtract the first terms one from the other and write the answer as a pair in which the measuring unit remains the same.

(15,7)−(9,7)=(6,7)   because 15−9=6

(21,11)−(13,11)=(8,11)   because 21−13=8

Using the bar notation we can write:

$\frac{15}{7}-\frac{9}{7}=\frac{15-9}{7}=\frac{6}{7}$

$\frac{21}{11}-\frac{13}{11}=\frac{21-13}{11}=\frac{8}{11}$

Find the answers to the following subtractions:

(7,13)−(2,13)=   (11,23)−(6,23)=

(31,9)−(7,9)= $\frac{7}{15}-\frac{4}{15}=$

(8,19)−$\frac{7}{19}$= $\frac{11}{12}-(5,12)=$

Addition and subtraction of fractions

11. Let us now use the idea of equivalence for the solution of the problem of addition of fractions.

If we have (7,18)+(6,18) we know it is [(7+6),18].

We need the extra brackets to show clearly which are the terms of the resultant ordered pair.

16

But $(6,18)=(1,3)$. So if we are given $(7,18)+(1,3)$ we must think of all the equivalent fractions of $(1,3)$ and choose the one whose second term is equal to 18.

We therefore proceed as follows:

$(7,18)+(1,3)=(7,18)+(6,18)=([7+6],18)=(13,18)$

We could, if we wished, write down as many of the fractions equivalent to $(1,3)$ as we need until we get to one with a second term equal to 18:

$(1,3)=(2,6)=(3,9)=(4,12)=(5,15)=(6,18)$.

But since we know that $3 \times 6 = 18$ and that $(1 \times 6, 3 \times 6)=(1,3)$, we can save time.

If we were given $(7,25)+(3,5)$, we should proceed as follows:

$(7,25)+(3,5)$
$=(7,25)+(3 \times 5, 5 \times 5)$
$=(7,25)+(15,25)$
$=(22,25)$

We see at once that 5×5, that is, multiplying the second term of the second fraction by 5, gives us the second term of the first fraction.

Similarly, if we are given $(3,7)+(5,21)$, we proceed by replacing $(3,7)$ by its equivalent $(9,21)$ and then add 9 and 5.

The answer is $(14,21)$ or $(2,3)$.

Find the answers to:

$(7,12)+(5,36)=$
$(1,14)+(3,28)=$
$(3,16)+(5,8)=$
$(9,11)+(23,33)=$
$(15,64)+(11,8)=$
$(1,15)+(2,5)=$
$(7,45)+(13,15)=$
$\frac{12}{15}+\frac{7}{60}=$
$\frac{14}{55}+\frac{1}{11}=$
$\frac{2}{21}+\frac{9}{42}=$
$\frac{19}{100}+\frac{9}{10}=$
$\frac{31}{57}+\frac{2}{19}=$
$(7,32)+\frac{1}{16}=$

17

12. The same procedure can be followed for subtraction. Find the answers to:

$(7,12)-(5,36)=$

$(5,8)-(3,16)=$

$\frac{14}{66}-\frac{1}{11}=$

$\frac{9}{10}-\frac{17}{100}=$

13. We can of course add more than two fractions together so long as it is possible to find fractions equivalent to the given ones which all possess the same measuring unit.

$(2,7)+(3,14)+(9,28)=(8,28)+(6,28)+(9,28)$

$=(2\times4, 7\times4)+(3\times2, 14\times2)+(9,28)$

$=[(8+6+9),28]$

$=(23,28)$

We can even have a mixture of additions and subtractions and operate in a similar way.

$(2,7)-(3,14)+(9,28)$

$=(8,28)-(6,28)+(9,28)$

$=[(8-6+9),28]$

$=(11,28)$

Find the answers to:

$(1,15)+\frac{7}{30}-\frac{1}{5}=$

$(3,5)-\frac{9}{10}+\frac{7}{20}=$

14. What happens if the two measuring rods are not, as above, one a multiple of the other? If we were asked to add $(5,7)$ and $(7,9)$, for example, what could we do?

Among the fractions equivalent to $(5,7)$ we have:

$\frac{5}{7}=\frac{10}{14}=\frac{15}{21}=\frac{20}{28}=\frac{25}{35}=\frac{30}{42}=\frac{35}{49}=\frac{40}{56}=\frac{45}{63}=\frac{50}{70}= \ldots$

and among those equivalent to $(7,9)$ we have:

$\frac{7}{9}=\frac{14}{18}=\frac{21}{27}=\frac{28}{36}=\frac{35}{45}=\frac{42}{54}=\frac{49}{63}=\frac{56}{72}=\frac{63}{81}= \ldots$

There are two, $\frac{45}{63}$ and $\frac{49}{63}$ which possess the same measuring unit, namely 63. We can therefore add them as follows:

$(5,7)+(7,9)=(45,63)+(49,63)=[(45+49),63)]=(94,63)$

18

Do we need to write down all the equivalent fractions in a family until we reach those we want? No, for

$(5,7)+(7,9)=$
$$=(5\times9,\ 7\times9)+(7\times7,\ 9\times7)$$
$$=(45,63)+(49,63)$$

would lead us to the answer directly.

Can you say why this short cut is correct and how you could have found it?

Apply a similar procedure to the following additions:

$(2,3)+(4,5)=$
$(7,8)+(5,9)=$
$(1,11)+(3,7)=$
$(2,9)+(1,13)=$
$(4,7)+(3,10)=$
$\frac{1}{3}+\frac{2}{5}=$
$\frac{3}{7}+\frac{2}{11}=$
$\frac{4}{9}+\frac{3}{10}=$
$\frac{2}{13}+\frac{1}{6}=$
$\frac{5}{12}+\frac{7}{5}=$

In the case of subtractions we operate in the same way. Find the answers to:

$\frac{2}{9}-\frac{1}{13}=$
$\frac{7}{8}-\frac{5}{9}=$
$\frac{3}{7}-\frac{1}{11}=$
$(4,5)-(4,7)=$
$(5,6)-(4,7)=$
$(4,7)-(3,10)=$

15. If we write two fractions *at random*, their second terms may have a common factor. Does this make the additions or subtractions more difficult?

Let us take an example:

$(7,\ 18)+(5,\ 27)$

We can write

$(7,\ 18)+(5,\ 27)=$
$$=(7,\ 2\times9)+(5,\ 3\times9)$$

$$=(7\times3,\ 2\times9\times3)+(5\times2,\ 3\times9\times2)$$
$$=(21,\ 54)+(10,\ 54)$$
$$=(31,\ 54)$$

Here we have made use of the fact that 9 is a common factor of 18 and 27 to give us a short cut for finding the equivalent fractions we need for our addition. $18=2\times9$ and $27=3\times9$. So to obtain a unit of measurement that contains both 18 and 27 all we need to do is to choose 54 which is $2\times9\times3$ or $3\times9\times2$, i.e., 6×9. We see that 6 contains 2 which is the other factor of 18 and also 3 which is the other factor of 27. Having found a common measuring rod in this way we can then perform the addition as above.

Is this principle always true when we are confronted with such fractions? Write down several and make sure whether what we have just done can always be done.

Since, when finding the equivalent fractions that enable us to complete the addition, we look for those that have the same second term, and since in the two families there are many such cases, we choose the first, which is also the smallest.

For example

$$\tfrac{7}{18}=\tfrac{14}{36}=\tfrac{21}{54}=\tfrac{28}{72}=\tfrac{35}{90}=\tfrac{42}{108}=\tfrac{49}{126}=\tfrac{56}{144}=\tfrac{63}{162}\cdots$$
$$\tfrac{5}{27}=\tfrac{10}{54}=\tfrac{15}{81}=\tfrac{20}{108}=\tfrac{25}{135}=\tfrac{30}{162}=\tfrac{35}{189}=\tfrac{40}{216}\cdots$$

Here 54, 108, 162 all give a common measuring unit, and we should find more if we proceeded further; but 54 is the *lowest common multiple* of 18 and 27.

The lowest common multiple of the units of measurement of the two fractions to be added (or subtracted) gives us the means by which we can perform our additions (or subtractions) of these fractions.

Lowest common multiple

16. How do we find the L.C.M. (or lowest common multiple) of any two numbers?

We already know how to find the common factors of two numbers.

The L.C.M. will contain the common factors, but since it must be a multiple of each of the numbers it will also contain the factors that are not common to the two numbers.

Let us find a few L.C.M's of two numbers.

18 and 27	$18=2\times9$	$27=3\times9$	L.C.M.$=2\times3\times9$
16 and 24	$16=2\times8$	$24=3\times8$	L.C.M.$=2\times3\times8$
15 and 25	$15=3\times5$	$25=5\times5$	L.C.M.$=3\times5\times5$
18 and 24			
25 and 35			
18 and 45			
91 and 35			
38 and 57			

17. We now have all we need to add any fractions or subtract any one fraction from any other using a short cut. We can always use the families of equivalent fractions if we are not sure.

Let us see how much time we can save by working on the following examples using the various ways we know. Time yourself only after you have written down the questions.

$\frac{5}{24}+\frac{7}{36}=$

$(2,34)+(19,51)=$

$(1,28)+(8,35)=$

$\frac{7}{22}-\frac{4}{33}=$

$(3,35)+(7,45)=$

Now use the shortest method to find the answers to:

$\frac{1}{11}+\frac{3}{22}+\frac{5}{33}=$

$\frac{8}{35}+\frac{6}{77}=$

$(3,19)+(5,38)+(2,57)=$

$(14,39)-(3,57)=$

Algebra of equivalent pairs

18. Let us take two equivalent fractions, say $\frac{2}{4}$ and $\frac{3}{6}$ and use the four rods red, pink, light and dark green to represent them.

If we add the smaller and also the bigger rods together, we find a new pair $\frac{2+3}{4+6}$ (i.e. the pair yellow, orange) which also belongs to the family. Similarly, if we subtract 2 from 3 and 4 from 6 we get the pair (1,2) which belongs to the family.

Is this always true for the family equivalent to $\frac{1}{2}$?

If (a,b) is any fraction of this family, what do we know of these two numbers a and b?

If (c,d) is another of the same family, what do we know of the two numbers c and d?

Let $(a+c, b+d)$ be the new pair obtained by adding a to c and b to d. What do we know of $a+c$ and $b+d$?

To decide all these questions you can make use of the rods.

If we take three equivalent fractions $(a,b)=(c,d)=(e,f)$
What can you say of $a+c+e$ and $b+d+f$?
What can you say of $a+c-e$ and $b+d-f$?
What can you say of $a-c+e$ and $b-d+f$?

Since $\frac{1}{2}$ is the irreducible fraction of this family, any other fraction of the family can be written as $(n, 2 \times n)$ where n is any whole number.

Are $(m, 2 \times m)$, $(p, 2 \times p)$, $(z, 2 \times z)$ members of this family?

Make use of your rods to decide.

If $\frac{2}{3}$ is the irreducible fraction of the family, can you write any other fraction in it using letters as we have just been doing?

Are $(2 \times p, 3 \times p)$, $(2 \times y, 3 \times y)$ also members of that family?

Make use of your rods if you cannot decide.

Write a few members of the following families:
$(2,7)=(4,14)=(6,21)= \ldots$
$(3,8)=(6,16)=(9,24)= \ldots$
$(15,11)=(30,22)=(45,33)= \ldots$
using letters as above.

Equivalence—A

19. If $\frac{K}{H}$ or (K,H) is the irreducible fraction of a family, can you say whether $(3 \times K, 3 \times H)$, $(12 \times K, 12 \times H)$, $(73 \times K, 73 \times H)$ are members of the family?

If n is any whole number, is $(n \times K, n \times H)$ also a member of that family?

Make with your rods any two lengths and call one K and the other one H. If you measure the first with the second you get the fraction $\frac{K}{H}$ or the ordered pair (K,H). How would you get the family of the fractions equivalent to (K,H)? Does this help you to decide the questions put to you at the beginning of this section?

Cross multiplication and equivalence

20. If (a,b) is a fraction, is $(n \times a, n \times b)$ a member of the same family? is $(m \times a, m \times b)$ also one?

and $[(n+m) \times a, (n+m) \times b]$?

and $[(n-m) \times a, (n-m) \times b]$?

Now let us take two equivalent pairs (a,b) and (c,d).

We have $\frac{a}{b} = \frac{c}{d}$. Can you multiply $a \times d$ and $b \times c$ when a, b, c and d are given numbers?

What do you find? When we do this, we say we **cross multiply**. Try it out on several examples.

Is it true that cross multiplying two equivalent fractions always gives two equal products?

When we have equivalent fractions we know that both can be obtained from the irreducible pair in the family by multiplying each of its two terms by the same number. Does this help you to solve the question just put to you?

If we write $\frac{K}{H}$ or (K,H) for the irreducible fraction of the family, we have $(a,b) = (n \times K, n \times H)$

$$\text{and } (c,d) = (m \times K, m \times H)$$

Cross multiply: $a \times d = n \times K \times m \times H$

$$\text{and } b \times c = n \times H \times m \times K$$

Are these two products equal?

23

21. Can you say whether the following fractions are equivalent, first by cross multiplication and then by finding the irreducible fraction of the family?

$\frac{3}{17}$ and $\frac{15}{85}$	$\frac{35}{55}$ and $\frac{40}{77}$	$\frac{57}{81}$ and $\frac{38}{34}$
$\frac{33}{88}$ and $\frac{39}{104}$	$\frac{45}{63}$ and $\frac{55}{99}$	$\frac{117}{104}$ and $\frac{81}{72}$
$\frac{8}{16}$ and $\frac{7}{16}$	$\frac{39}{25}$ and $\frac{39}{24}$	$\frac{54}{153}$ and $\frac{18}{51}$
$\frac{34}{26}$ and $\frac{51}{39}$	$\frac{15}{32}$ and $\frac{17}{33}$	$\frac{21}{75}$ and $\frac{27}{100}$

Inequalities

22. When two fractions are not equivalent they are said to be **unequal**.

Let us take the pairs (1,2) and (1,3) or a half and a third. They can be replaced by their equivalents, (3,6) and (2,6). Because 3 is greater than 2 we can say that $\frac{1}{2}$ is greater than $\frac{1}{3}$ and write $\frac{1}{2} > \frac{1}{3}$ or $\frac{1}{3} < \frac{1}{2}$ which we read as '$\frac{1}{3}$ is less than $\frac{1}{2}$'.

If we want to **compare** two fractions and find whether one is smaller, equal, or greater than the other, we must first find the equivalent ones which have the same measuring unit. We have seen in No. 15 that this is done by finding the L.C.M. of the second terms.

Compare:

$\frac{5}{8}$ and $\frac{5}{7}$	$\frac{3}{4}$ and $\frac{4}{5}$	$\frac{3}{5}$ and $\frac{4}{7}$
$\frac{7}{8}$ and $\frac{9}{11}$	$\frac{13}{12}$ and $\frac{12}{11}$	$\frac{15}{13}$ and $\frac{15}{12}$

If fractions have the same first terms but different second terms, which is greater?

Compare:

$\frac{7}{11}$ and $\frac{7}{13}$	$\frac{5}{12}$ and $\frac{5}{9}$	$\frac{11}{10}$ and $\frac{11}{12}$

If fractions have the same second terms but different first terms, which is the smaller?

Compare:

$\frac{3}{7}$ and $\frac{4}{7}$	$\frac{11}{17}$ and $\frac{14}{17}$	$\frac{34}{95}$ and $\frac{73}{95}$

Can you cross multiply $\frac{5}{11}$ and $\frac{5}{12}$? Which is the smaller of the products? Does it tell you something about how to compare fractions by cross multiplication?

24

Use this method to decide the questions above and see which is the shortest way.

Transformations of pairs

23.   Let us start with a pair of rods, say a tan and an orange. If we put a white rod

1) end to end with the orange, is the fraction obtained greater or smaller than the one we started with?

2) end to end with the tan one, is the fraction obtained greater or smaller than the one we started with?

3) end to end with each of the rods, is the fraction obtained greater or smaller than the one we started with?

Take other pairs and choose either a white or a red or a light green rod and repeat what we have just done. Can you decide the questions? Can you say what happens to a fraction:

1) when we increase the second term but not the first?

2) when we increase the first term but not the second?

3) when we increase the two terms *by the same amount*?

24.   Fractions with the two terms equal form a family in which the irreducible fraction is (1,1) or $\frac{1}{1}$. We shall write as we did in No. 9: (1,1)=$\frac{1}{1}$=1 and call this **the unit.**

We can compare any fraction to the unit as we compared any fraction to any other one.

When will a fraction be smaller than the unit? When will it be greater?

Sometimes the latter fractions are called *improper* while the first are called *proper*. We shall not refer to them in this way in this book.

Sometimes the first term of the fraction is called its **numerator** and the second term its **denominator.**

Using these words, express the results of your comparisons of a fraction with the unit.

25. If we start with a fraction smaller than the unit and add one to each of its terms, what happens to the fraction? If we go on adding one to each of its terms, what do you observe about the fractions you obtain?

26. If we start with a fraction greater than the unit and add one to each of its terms, what happens to the fraction? If we go on adding one to each of its terms, what do you observe about the fractions you obtain?

27. Start with any fraction and subtract one from each of its terms. What happens to the fraction?

How often can you do these subtractions and what do you observe if the fraction is:

1) smaller than the unit
2) greater than the unit
3) equivalent to the unit?

Ratios and proportions

28. Let us take four rods so that they form two pairs of equivalent fractions, for example (2,4) and (5,10). We can form with them the following pairs:

(2,5), (10,4)	(5,2), (4,10)	(5,2), (10,4)
(2,10), (5,4)	(2,10), (4,5)	(10,2), (5,4)
(10,2), (4,5)	(4,2), (5,10)	(4,2), (10,5)
(2,4), (5,10)	(2,4), (10,5)	(2,5), (4,10)

Which of these pairs are equivalent?

Put a red rod against a pink and a yellow against an orange. Then put these two pairs against each other so that the red is on the yellow and the pink on the orange. The four rods can be held together and turned round so that they are seen in the four following positions:

(i) red, pink   (ii) pink, orange
    yellow, orange   red, yellow

(iii) orange, yellow	(iv) yellow, red
pink, red	orange, pink

In figures we can write these as:

· (2,4), (5,10)	(4,10), (2,5)
(10,5), (4,2)	(5,2), (10,4)

Are these pairs of pairs equivalent?

Does what we have found depend on the fact that we chose these particular rods, or upon the fact that we started with two equivalent pairs?

When we want to talk about what makes the elements in each pair belong to a family of equivalence, we say that they are in a certain **ratio**. Thus $\frac{1}{2}$, or $\frac{2}{4}$, or $\frac{5}{10}$ are in the ratio of 1 to 2.

We know that if the two pairs are (a,b) and (c,d), and are equivalent, we have $(a,b)=(c,d)$ and

(i) $a \times d = b \times c$

But the following products can also be written:

(ii) $b \times c = d \times a$

(iii) $d \times a = c \times b$

(iv) $c \times b = a \times d$

and for each of these four products we can write the corresponding equivalent pair:

(i) $(a,b)=(c,d)$	(ii) $(b,d)=(a,c)$
(iii) $(d,c)=(b,a)$	(iv) $(c,a)=(d,b)$

Two pairs of equivalent fractions are said to form a **proportion**, and we have just found that from any proportion we can obtain three others.

We already know that (b,a) is the reciprocal of (a,b), so (i) and (iii) above say that *if two fractions are equivalent their reciprocals are equivalent.*

What can you say of (ii) and (iv) above?

Write in bar notation what we have just found.

29.   If we start with a proportion, as we did in No. 28, do we find a new one when we increase the denominator in each pair by adding to it its numerator?

For example, if we choose the red on the pink and the yellow on the orange and increase the pink by the length of the red and the orange by the length of the yellow, we get red on dark green and yellow on orange and yellow end. to end. Are these new fractions equivalent?

$\frac{2}{4}$ and $\frac{5}{15}$ are both equivalent to $\frac{1}{3}$, so the answer is 'yes'.

If $\frac{a}{b}$ is equivalent to $\frac{c}{d}$, do we always have $\frac{a}{b+a}$ equivalent to $\frac{c}{c+d}$?

By cross multiplying we get

$a \times (c+d)$ and $c \times (b+a)$ or $a \times c + a \times d$ and $c \times b + c \times a$.

But we know that $a \times d$ equals $c \times b$. The two products of the cross-multiplication are equal.

We know also that there are four proportions for every pair of equivalent fractions, so that many new relationships can be obtained. Can you write them?

Can you subtract instead of adding in the formation of new proportions?

Is $\frac{a}{b-a}$ equivalent to $\frac{c}{d-c}$? or is $\frac{a}{c-a}$ equivalent to $\frac{b}{d-b}$?

Use your rods first to make sure you understand what you are being asked and then see whether the writing corresponds to what you have been doing.

Equivalence—M

30. We formed families of equivalent fractions by taking the same number of each of the rods that formed the pair with which we started.

We shall now see that if one rod is measured by a second rod, this can be measured by a third.

Take a red and a light green rod. The first is $\frac{2}{3}$ of the second, but the light green can be measured by the yellow and is $\frac{3}{5}$ of it.

If we take these three rods—red, light green and yellow— and make a triplet by placing them side by side in that order, we see that we can measure the red directly by the yellow, finding that it is $\frac{2}{5}$ of it. But we can also measure the red by the light green ($\frac{2}{3}$) and then the light green by the yellow ($\frac{3}{5}$). So, the red rod has two names: $\frac{2}{5}$ of the yellow (when directly compared with the yellow) and $\frac{2}{3}$ of $\frac{3}{5}$ of the yellow (when using the light green as intermediary). Thus we can write:

$\frac{2}{5}$ is equivalent to $\frac{2}{3}$ of $\frac{3}{5}$

If we turn the triplet around and measure the yellow by the light green and the light green by the red, we have:

$\frac{5}{2}$ is equivalent to $\frac{5}{3}$ of $\frac{3}{2}$

31. Let us gain experience in reading these triplets (and the variations we get by merely changing the order of the rods).

Write down in figures what you find. Form the triplet red, yellow, black and measure the first by the second, the second by the third and then the first by the third, noting the equivalence you find as we did above.

Do it again with these triplets:

black, orange, light green	dark green, yellow, blue
red, blue, black	orange, pink, blue

32. In fact there is no reason why we should only take three rods. If we have, say, four: a red, a yellow, a black and a blue rod, we can put them side by side and measure the red directly by the blue ($\frac{2}{9}$) or the red by the yellow ($\frac{2}{5}$), the yellow by the black ($\frac{5}{7}$), the black by the blue ($\frac{7}{9}$). We have:

$\frac{2}{9}$ is equivalent to $\frac{2}{5}$ of $\frac{5}{7}$ of $\frac{7}{9}$

Do the same with any four rods. Repeat this, changing the rods used, until you have no doubt about the reading and writing of the equivalences concerned.

33. Instead of four, take five, or six, or any number of rods and write down what you read for the equivalences.

Let us take the staircase formed of the ten rods in increasing order. If we measure the white directly by the orange we get $\frac{1}{10}$; if we use the intermediaries we get:

$\frac{1}{10}$ is equivalent to $\frac{1}{2}$ of $\frac{2}{3}$ of $\frac{3}{4}$ of $\frac{4}{5}$ of $\frac{5}{6}$ of $\frac{6}{7}$ of $\frac{7}{8}$ of $\frac{8}{9}$ of $\frac{9}{10}$

Rearrange the ten rods and write down the equivalences each arrangement presents. When reading such fractions as $\frac{2}{1}$ or $\frac{3}{2}$ remember that we do not say 'oneth' and 'twoth', but 'ones' and 'halves'.

34. We shall now write this new equivalence using the ordered pairs notation.

Let $a, b, c \ldots h, k$ be any lengths. We can write (a,k) is equivalent to (a,b) of (b,c) of (c,d) of $\ldots$ of (h,k). In fact the triplet a, b, c gives three pairs in this order (a,b), (b,c), (a,c) and the last is called the *contracted* form of (a,b) of (b,c).

We see that we can expand an ordered pair as above by inserting any number of intermediaries, or contract any suitable sequence of pairs to one.

Expand :

(2,7) using the lengths 13, 11, 8, 9, as intermediaries

(3,17) using the lengths 4, 15, 7, 19, 21, 5

(13,10) using the lengths 3, 5, 14, 9, 2, 11, 34, 17

(21,73) using the lengths 19, 3, 29, 37, 44, 5, 24, 56, 81, 92

Contract :

$\frac{21}{17}$ of $\frac{17}{35}$ of $\frac{35}{19}$ of $\frac{19}{5}$

$\frac{7}{11}$ of $\frac{11}{13}$ of $\frac{13}{9}$ of $\frac{9}{23}$ of $\frac{23}{15}$

$\frac{4}{5}$ of $\frac{5}{8}$ of $\frac{8}{11}$ of $\frac{11}{12}$ of $\frac{12}{18}$ of $\frac{18}{16}$ of $\frac{16}{7}$ of $\frac{7}{8}$

$\frac{31}{16}$ of $\frac{16}{27}$ of $\frac{27}{13}$ of $\frac{13}{25}$ of $\frac{25}{19}$ of $\frac{19}{201}$ of $\frac{201}{77}$ of $\frac{77}{30}$ of $\frac{30}{9}$ of $\frac{9}{26}$

Fraction of a fraction

35. We know what (2,3) of (3,5) is. What would you say (2,3) of (4,5) is?

In order to apply the method of Nos. 32-34 we must have two fractions such that the second term of the first is equal to the first term of the second. Can we find two fractions equivalent respectively to (2,3) and (4,5) and having the 'middle' terms equal?

$$\tfrac{2}{3}=\tfrac{6}{9}=\tfrac{8}{12}=\tfrac{10}{15}=\ \ldots$$
$$\tfrac{4}{5}=\tfrac{8}{10}=\tfrac{12}{15}=\tfrac{16}{20}=\ \ldots$$

In these families $\tfrac{8}{12}$ and $\tfrac{12}{15}$ have the same 'middle' term and 12 is the L.C.M. of 3 and 4.

So (2,3) of (4,5)=(8,12) of (12,15)=(8,15) by contraction.

(We shall now always write = for 'is equivalent to').

Find what are:

$$\tfrac{1}{9}\ \text{of}\ \tfrac{3}{5}$$
$$\tfrac{2}{7}\ \text{of}\ \tfrac{1}{3}$$
$$\tfrac{4}{3}\ \text{of}\ \tfrac{5}{7}$$

and also find what are:

$$\tfrac{3}{5}\ \text{of}\ \tfrac{1}{9}$$
$$\tfrac{1}{3}\ \text{of}\ \tfrac{2}{7}$$
$$\tfrac{6}{11}\ \text{of}\ \tfrac{4}{3}$$

36. Say how you find a **fraction of a fraction** when the two are given.

If (a,b) is any fraction and (c,d) another, can you repeat the procedure with these fractions in order to find what (a,b) of (c,d) is? What would you find for (c,d) of (a,b)?

37. Sometimes, instead of the expression 'of' between two fractions, the sign $\times$ is used.

$\tfrac{2}{3}\times\tfrac{4}{5}$ can be read '$\tfrac{2}{3}$ of $\tfrac{4}{5}$' or '$\tfrac{2}{3}$ multiplied by $\tfrac{4}{5}$'. We shall use either of these two ways from now on.

Can you find what $\tfrac{2}{3}$ of $\tfrac{4}{5}$ of $\tfrac{7}{11}$ is?

$\tfrac{2}{3}$ of $\tfrac{4}{5}$ is $\tfrac{8}{15}$, so you now only need to find what $\tfrac{8}{15}$ of $\tfrac{7}{11}$ is.

Is $\tfrac{8}{15}$ of $\tfrac{7}{11}$ equivalent to $\tfrac{56}{165}$?

Find the fraction equivalent to:

$$\tfrac{3}{2}\ \text{of}\ \tfrac{5}{4}\ \text{of}\ \tfrac{11}{7} \qquad\qquad \tfrac{11}{7}\times\tfrac{3}{2}\times\tfrac{5}{4}$$
$$\tfrac{5}{4}\times\tfrac{11}{7}\times\tfrac{3}{2}$$

$\frac{3}{4} \times \frac{2}{3} \times \frac{8}{9}$ and then find the **product** derived from these by merely changing the order

$\frac{11}{10} \times \frac{9}{12} \times \frac{5}{22}$ and then the product derived from these by merely changing the order

$\frac{1}{3} \times \frac{1}{4} \times \frac{1}{4} \times \frac{1}{3}$

$\frac{1}{2} \times \frac{1}{3} \times \frac{1}{4} \times \frac{1}{5}$

$\frac{2}{3} \times \frac{4}{5} \times \frac{6}{7} \times \frac{7}{8}$

When you have found the product can you find the irreducible fraction of its family?

38. What do you get if you take a fraction and its own reciprocal, for example $\frac{1}{2}$ of $\frac{2}{1}$, $\frac{3}{2}$ of $\frac{2}{3}$, $\frac{7}{5}$ of $\frac{5}{7}$, $\frac{11}{13}$ of $\frac{13}{11}$?

If (a,b) is any fraction, (b,a) its reciprocal, (a,b) of (b,a) $=(a \times b, b \times a)$ which is equivalent to $(1,1)$.

Or $\quad \frac{a}{b} \times \frac{b}{a} = \frac{a \times b}{b \times a} = \frac{1}{1} = 1$

Now let us multiply a fraction first by (a,b) and then by (b,a), its reciprocal. We get

$$\frac{K}{H} \times \frac{a}{b} = \frac{K \times a}{H \times b} \qquad \frac{K \times a}{H \times b} \times \frac{b}{a} = \frac{K \times a \times b}{H \times a \times b} = \frac{K}{H}$$

Thus we are back where we started:

$\star\ (K,H) \times (a,b) \times (b,a) = (K,H)$

We have used the sign $\times$ between two fractions instead of the word 'of'.

If we take the fraction equivalent to the product of two fractions, each of these two can be obtained from the product by *dividing* by the other.

$(K \times a, H \times b) \div (K, H) = (a, b)$
$(K \times a, H \times b) \div (a, b) = (K, H)$

Here the sign $\div$ is read 'divided by' and only means that we look at the operation $\times$ from the other end.

$$\begin{array}{l} (K, H) \times (a, b) = (K \times a, H \times b) \\ \text{and } (K \times a, H \times b) \div (a, b) = (K, H) \\ \text{and } (K \times a, H \times b) \div (K, H) = (a, b) \end{array}$$

are three forms of the same relation.

But, using the formula marked ★ on p. 32:

$$(K, H) \times (a, b) = (K, H) \div (b, a)$$
$$\text{or } (K, H) \div (b, a) = (K, H) \times (a, b)$$

Find:

$\frac{2}{3} \div \frac{4}{5}$	$\frac{3}{2} \div \frac{7}{11}$
$\frac{7}{3} \div \frac{5}{8}$	$\frac{4}{9} \div \frac{1}{5}$
$\frac{11}{12} \div \frac{5}{4}$	$\frac{12}{9} \div \frac{3}{5}$
$\frac{7}{12} \div \frac{4}{3}$	$\frac{15}{24} \div \frac{1}{12}$

Can you say in words what you have had to do to divide a fraction by a fraction?

Mixed numbers

39. Let us now measure the orange rod using the light green as our unit.

How many do we need?

We have $10 = 3 \times 3 + 1$ for the orange (if we are using the white rod as our unit). But the white one is $\frac{1}{3}$ of the light green, then the orange is 3 and $\frac{1}{3}$ of the light green rod. We shall write $3\frac{1}{3}$ for the measure of the orange using three light green rods and the white. We also know that $\frac{10}{3}$ is the same measure of the orange using ten white rods, each being $\frac{1}{3}$ of the light green. These ways of writing are equivalent: $3\frac{1}{3}$ is the same value as $\frac{10}{3}$ since both mean that we measure the orange rod with the light green.

When we write $3\frac{1}{3}$ instead of $(10,3)$ or $\frac{10}{3}$ we say we use the **mixed number** form of that fraction; 3 is called the **whole part** and $\frac{1}{3}$ the **fractional part**.

Change into fractions the following mixed numbers:

$$2\frac{1}{2} \quad 1\frac{1}{3} \quad 8\frac{1}{4} \quad 3\frac{2}{3} \quad 4\frac{1}{2} \quad 4\frac{1}{5} \quad 5\frac{1}{2} \quad 6\frac{2}{3} \quad 7\frac{1}{5}$$

Change into mixed numbers the following fractions:

$$\frac{7}{2} \quad \frac{3}{2} \quad \frac{4}{3} \quad \frac{7}{5} \quad \frac{6}{4} \quad \frac{9}{8} \quad \frac{10}{4} \quad \frac{11}{3} \quad \frac{12}{5} \quad \frac{13}{7} \quad \frac{19}{10} \quad \frac{21}{8} \quad \frac{32}{19}$$

Operations on mixed numbers

40. All operations with fractions can be done with mixed numbers.

Note that $2\frac{1}{2}$ can be read 'two and a half' or '$2+\frac{1}{2}$'.

Read $7\frac{2}{3}$ $4\frac{1}{7}$ $5\frac{4}{5}$ $10\frac{8}{9}$ $14\frac{1}{6}$ $31\frac{1}{2}$ $6\frac{3}{7}$ $42\frac{9}{11}$

Read the following:

$$2\tfrac{1}{3}+4\tfrac{1}{3}=6\tfrac{2}{3} \qquad\qquad 3\tfrac{2}{5}+4\tfrac{1}{5}=7\tfrac{3}{5}$$
$$4\tfrac{1}{2}+3\tfrac{1}{3}=7+\tfrac{1}{2}+\tfrac{1}{3}=7\tfrac{5}{6}$$
$$4\tfrac{1}{4}-2\tfrac{1}{4}=2$$
$$4\tfrac{1}{2}-3\tfrac{1}{4}=1\tfrac{1}{4}$$
$$7\tfrac{1}{4}-3\tfrac{1}{2}=3\tfrac{3}{4}$$

Can you say how all these calculations were done?

Can you do the following?

$$7\tfrac{1}{2}-5\tfrac{3}{4}= \qquad\qquad 11\tfrac{3}{4}-9\tfrac{4}{5}=$$
$$4\tfrac{3}{4}+6\tfrac{2}{3}= \qquad\qquad 2\tfrac{1}{2}+3\tfrac{2}{3}+4\tfrac{3}{4}=$$

Equivalent expressions for pairs

41.   When we measure the two rods of the pair light green, orange we can find many ways of writing the relationship between them depending on our choice of the unit.

If we use the white one we have the fraction $\frac{3}{10}$.

If we use the red rod $\dfrac{1\frac{1}{2}}{5}$

light green rod $\dfrac{1}{3\frac{1}{3}}$

pink rod $\dfrac{\frac{3}{4}}{2\frac{1}{2}}$

yellow rod $\dfrac{\frac{3}{5}}{2}$

So we have:

$$\frac{3}{10}=\frac{1\frac{1}{2}}{5}=\frac{1}{3\frac{1}{3}}=\frac{\frac{3}{4}}{2\frac{1}{2}}=\frac{\frac{3}{5}}{2}=\;\cdots$$

Complete the series using the five rods left.

Can you write the relationship of the black to the orange using as unit of measurement each of the ten rods in turn?

Do the same for the following pairs of rods:

yellow, tan	dark green, black	tan, blue
red, black	pink, blue	orange, black

42. In this book we have learned many ways of working with fractions. In particular we have seen why we can use many ways of writing them. Because we are always considering families of equivalent fractions we have been able to find an answer to every problem we have met.

Now what is $\frac{3}{4}$ of $2\frac{1}{2}$? Since $2\frac{1}{2}$ is $\frac{5}{2}$ we know the answer is $\frac{15}{8}$. Can we divide $7\frac{3}{4}$ by $2\frac{1}{2}$? Since $7\frac{3}{4}$ is $\frac{31}{4}$ and $2\frac{1}{2}$ is $\frac{5}{2}$, we know the answer: $\frac{31}{4} \div \frac{5}{2} = \frac{31}{4} \times \frac{2}{5} = \frac{31}{10}$ or $3\frac{1}{10}$.

43. We have found that for addition and multiplication of fractions we can change the order in which we meet the fractions without changing the result. Can we do the same for subtraction and division?

For example, is $\frac{3}{4} \div 2\frac{1}{2}$ equivalent to $2\frac{1}{2} \div \frac{3}{4}$?

Is $7\frac{1}{2} - 2\frac{1}{2}$ equivalent to $2\frac{1}{2} - 7\frac{1}{2}$?

44. What happens when we subtract a fraction from itself?

$2\frac{1}{2} - 2\frac{1}{2} =$ $\frac{21}{9} - \frac{21}{9} =$ $(3,5) - (3,5) =$

What happens when we divide a fraction by itself?

$\frac{3}{4} \div \frac{3}{4} =$ $7\frac{1}{3} \div 7\frac{1}{3} =$ $(11,9) \div (11,9) =$

III

STUDY OF DECIMAL FRACTIONS

PART III

STUDY OF DECIMAL FRACTIONS

Defining a decimal fraction

1. In No. 41 in the previous Part we saw that if we measure the light green and orange pair using different rods as the unit, we can write the same relationship in different ways.

If the white is taken as the unit, the light green is $\frac{3}{10}$ of the orange. When we use the orange rod as measuring rod, we shall now write the light green as ·3.

This notation stands for $\frac{\frac{3}{10}}{1}$, and we read it 'point 3'.

It is a normal practice to write 0·3 and read it 'nought point 3'.

This is *not a new fraction;* it is a *new way of writing* the fraction when the orange rod (taken as 10) is the measuring rod. It is called **decimal notation.**

Write in decimal notation the measure of each of the rods, remembering that the orange is the measuring rod.

2. When we measure any rod by itself we write (1,1) or 1, as we have seen in No. 24 of the previous part.

When the orange is measured by itself we can write 1· or 1·0 with a dot after the 1 if we want to show that we are using the decimal notation. 1· or 1·0 *is equal to* 1 *and conversely.*

Since we know that $\frac{11}{10}$ is equal to $\frac{10}{10}+\frac{1}{10}$ we shall write in the decimal notation $\frac{11}{10}=1\cdot1$ or **one point one.**

Write similarly all the fractions in which the orange rod is the measuring rod and the lengths measured are equal to 12, 13, . . . 19 white rods.

$\frac{20}{10}$ we know is (2,1) or 2· In decimal notation it can be written 2·0 or 2·.

Write down the following fractions in decimal notation:

$$\frac{30}{10} \quad \frac{40}{10} \quad \frac{50}{10} \quad \frac{60}{10} \quad \frac{70}{10} \quad \frac{80}{10} \quad \frac{90}{10} \quad \frac{100}{10} \quad \frac{110}{10}$$

Translations of one notation to the other

3. Write down in decimal notation the following fractions:

$$\frac{21}{10} \quad \frac{23}{10} \quad \frac{25}{10} \quad \frac{27}{10} \quad \frac{29}{10}$$

$$\frac{32}{10} \quad \frac{35}{10} \quad \frac{36}{10} \quad \frac{37}{10} \quad \frac{38}{10}$$

$$\frac{41}{10} \quad \frac{42}{10} \quad \frac{44}{10} \quad \frac{47}{10} \quad \frac{49}{10}$$

$$\frac{53}{10} \quad \frac{54}{10} \quad \frac{56}{10} \quad \frac{58}{10} \quad \frac{59}{10}$$

$$\frac{61}{10} \quad \frac{63}{10} \quad \frac{65}{10} \quad \frac{68}{10} \quad \frac{69}{10}$$

$$\frac{72}{10} \quad \frac{73}{10} \quad \frac{74}{10} \quad \frac{75}{10} \quad \frac{76}{10}$$

$$\frac{81}{10} \quad \frac{83}{10} \quad \frac{85}{10} \quad \frac{87}{10} \quad \frac{89}{10}$$

$$\frac{92}{10} \quad \frac{94}{10} \quad \frac{96}{10} \quad \frac{98}{10} \quad \frac{102}{10}$$

$$\frac{105}{10} \quad \frac{109}{10} \quad \frac{111}{10} \quad \frac{115}{10} \quad \frac{121}{10}$$

4. Write as a fraction with denominator 10 the following decimal numbers:

·5	·7	·9	·3	·2
2·4	2·5	3·1	1·9	2·8
7·7	5·6	6·5	8·3	9·4
4·8	7·3	6·9	4·8	8·6
9·7	7·9	8·8	6·4	3·8
11·0	12·3	13·0	14·5	17·7
25·4	26·7	29·3	19·4	34·5
72·9	29·8	66·6	73·2	89·0
90·3	70·5	71·2	72·0	88·8
93·0	84·0	70·8	50·0	50·4

Operations on decimals

5. Since you can add $\frac{3}{10}+\frac{2}{10}$, can you add   ·3+ ·2

$$\frac{7}{10}+\frac{1}{10} \qquad\qquad ·7+ ·1$$
$$\frac{11}{10}+\frac{2}{10} \qquad\qquad 1·1+ ·2$$
$$\frac{17}{10}+\frac{13}{10} \qquad\qquad 1·7+1·3$$
$$\frac{19}{10}+\frac{12}{10} \qquad\qquad 1·9+1·2$$
$$\frac{7}{10}+\frac{32}{10} \qquad\qquad ·7+3·2$$
$$\frac{5}{10}+\frac{38}{10} \qquad\qquad ·5+3·8$$

Look at the following additions:

·3+·7	·4+·6	·8+·2	·1+·9
·7+·3	·6+·4	·2+·8	·9+·1

What do you see?

And what do the following show you?

·3+1·7	1·4+ ·6	1·8+·2	1·9+·1	1·5+·5
1·3+ ·7	·4+1·6	1·2+·8	1·1+·9	

And the following?

2·3+ ·7	2·3+1·7	2·3+2·7	2·3+5·7
3·8+ ·2	3·8+1·2	3·8+2·2	3·8+3·2
4·6+ ·4	4·6+1·4	4·6+4·4	4·6+5·4

40

6·7+ ·3	6·7+1·3	6·7+3·3	6·7+7·3
1·9+2·1	1·9+4·1	1·9+6·1	1·9+9·1

6. Since you can subtract $\frac{3}{10}-\frac{1}{10}$, can you subtract ·3—·1

$\frac{5}{10}-\frac{3}{10}$	·5—·3
$\frac{7}{10}-\frac{4}{10}$	·7—·4
$\frac{11}{10}-\frac{6}{10}$	1·1—·6
$\frac{15}{10}-\frac{9}{10}$	1·5—·9

Look at the following subtractions:

·7—·3	·6—·2	·8—·4	·9—·5	·5—·1
·9—·6	·7—·4	·6—·3	·4—·3	·8—·5
·9—·3	·6—·1	·7—·2	·9—·4	

What do you see?

Give the answers to the following subtractions:

1·7—·3	1·6—·2	1·8—·4	1·9—·5	1·5—·1
1·9—·6	1·7—·4	1·6—·3	1·4—·3	1·8—·5
1·8—·3	1·6—·1	1·7—·2	1·9—·4	

And to the following:

1·7—1·3	1·6—1·2	1·8—1·4	1·9—1·5
1·5—1·1	1·9—1·6	1·7—1·4	1·6—1·3
1·4—1·3	1·8—1·5	1·8—1·3	1·6—1·1
1·7—1·2	1·9—1·4		

When the answer is 0 you can write 0 or 0·0 or ·0 or 0·.

Give the answer to:

·9—·9	1·1—1·1	3·2—3·2	7·8—7·8

7. Subtract:

1·7— ·9	1·6— ·7	1·5— ·8	1·4— ·7
2·4—1·8	2·7—1·9	3·3—2·5	5·2—4·8
6·1—3·2	7·4—5·8	8·2—6·3	9·1—7·9

41

5·5—4·8	6·3—5·9	7·1—6·2	4·0—3·8
5·0—2·1	6·0—3·9	7·0—1·4	9·0—8·0

8. All these additions and subtractions can be written in the vertical form. We must put the dots one under the other and do just as before. Here are some additions worked out:

3·1	4·2	3·8	7·1	13·2
4·7	5·6	5·4	6·9	17·8
7·8	9·8	9·2	14·0	31·0

Give the answers to these additions:

5·4	6·3	7·1	8·2	10·3	21·4
4·5	3·6	2·9	3·8	10·8	32·5

34·5	32·9	38·4	36·6	44·7	59·9
35·8	44·3	41·5	35·3	56·4	48·7

What do you notice about the way of adding decimal numbers?

Give the answers to these subtractions:

7·8	9·8	9·2	14·0	31·0	32·7
—4·7	—4·2	—5·4	—6·9	—17·8	—13·8

What did you notice about the way you subtract decimal numbers?

9. Add the following columns of decimal numbers:

3·2	2·3	5·2	6·4	7·9	6·2
5·4	4·5	7·4	5·3	4·8	7·3
7·1	1·7	3·1	7·1	6·0	8·4
6·3	3·6	6·2	8·0	7·3	9·5

10·3	12·7	14·9	18·2	29·1	33·3
11·4	20·0	23·6	19·3	32·5	44·1
13·2	23·3	34·5	20·4	45·6	50·5
15·6	31·6	40·0	21·5	56·4	66·6

Check, adding upwards if you added downwards, or conversely.

Find the answers to the following horizontal additions:

7·2+4·4+6·2+1·5=
6·4+7·9+3·8+2·9=
7·7+6·3+2·3+1·1=
8·4+9·2+3·6+2·2=
7·6+6·7+6·5+5·6=

Check your answers, doing the addition in the opposite direction to that used at first.

Hundredths

10. If we use for our measuring length ten orange rods end to end we get the length equal to 100 white rods. We know that any other length made of rods end to end can be measured by that one and we can write our answers as:

(7,100) or $\frac{7}{100}$ if it is the black rod we are measuring
(23,100) or $\frac{23}{100}$ if it is the length 23 we are measuring

We shall now write these fractions in a new way, which is also called the decimal notation.

We can write $\frac{7}{100}$ as ·07 $\frac{23}{100}$ as ·23
$\frac{1}{100}$ as ·01 $\frac{11}{100}$ as ·11
$\frac{3}{100}$ as ·03 $\frac{99}{100}$ as ·99

Write the following fractions as decimals:

$\frac{8}{100}$	$\frac{4}{100}$	$\frac{6}{100}$	$\frac{5}{100}$	$\frac{2}{100}$	$\frac{9}{100}$	$\frac{12}{100}$
$\frac{17}{100}$	$\frac{19}{100}$	$\frac{21}{100}$	$\frac{27}{100}$	$\frac{34}{100}$	$\frac{38}{100}$	$\frac{44}{100}$
$\frac{46}{100}$	$\frac{50}{100}$	$\frac{60}{100}$	$\frac{68}{100}$	$\frac{71}{100}$	$\frac{51}{100}$	
$\frac{77}{100}$	$\frac{78}{100}$	$\frac{84}{100}$	$\frac{85}{100}$	$\frac{89}{100}$	$\frac{92}{100}$	$\frac{97}{100}$

Write the following decimals as fractions:

·02 ·05 ·07 ·18 ·25 ·28 ·33 ·40 ·53 ·56 ·67 ·88

Since $\frac{100}{100}$ is (1,1) or $\frac{1}{1}$ or 1, we shall also write it 1· or 1·0 or 1·00, and since $\frac{115}{100}=\frac{100}{100}+\frac{15}{100}$ we can write 1·15 for its decimal.

Give the decimal form of:

$\frac{117}{100}$ $\frac{123}{100}$ $\frac{144}{100}$ $\frac{150}{100}$ $\frac{165}{100}$ $\frac{170}{100}$ $\frac{184}{100}$ $\frac{193}{100}$ $\frac{199}{100}$

And the fractional form of:

1·18 1·29 1·36 1·48 1·59 1·60 1·72 1·80
1·86 1·90

11. Since $\frac{200}{100}=2$ we shall also write it as 2· or 2·0 or 2·00 and since $\frac{213}{100}=\frac{200}{100}+\frac{13}{100}$ we shall write 2·13 for its decimal.

Give the decimals for:

$\frac{300}{100}$ $\frac{400}{100}$ $\frac{500}{100}$ $\frac{600}{100}$ $\frac{700}{100}$ $\frac{800}{100}$ $\frac{900}{100}$ $\frac{209}{100}$ $\frac{218}{100}$

$\frac{22}{100}$ $\frac{234}{100}$ $\frac{245}{100}$ $\frac{256}{100}$ $\frac{274}{100}$ $\frac{285}{100}$ $\frac{301}{100}$ $\frac{308}{100}$ $\frac{315}{100}$

$\frac{325}{100}$ $\frac{354}{100}$ $\frac{366}{100}$ $\frac{377}{100}$ $\frac{393}{100}$ $\frac{406}{100}$ $\frac{405}{100}$ $\frac{416}{100}$ $\frac{436}{100}$

$\frac{463}{100}$ $\frac{475}{100}$ $\frac{485}{100}$ $\frac{499}{100}$ $\frac{503}{100}$ $\frac{606}{100}$ $\frac{702}{100}$ $\frac{803}{100}$ $\frac{901}{100}$

Give the fractional form of:

5·09 5·06 5·17 5·32 5·71 5·84 5·96 5·04
6·01 6·02 6·03 6·11 6·19 6·23 6·77 6·93
7·03 7·05 7·97 7·13 7·23 7·37 7·48 7·84
8·00 8·20 8·30 8·32 8·41 8·53 8·60 8·90
9·10 9·11 9·21 9·22 9·33 9·40 9·71 9·88

12. Since $\frac{1,000}{100}=10$, $\frac{1,100}{100}=11$, $\frac{2,000}{100}=20$ etc. . . . we can write them in the decimal forms 10· or 10·0 or 10·00; 11· or 11·0 or 11·00; 20· or 20·0 or 20·00.

Since $\frac{1,234}{100}=\frac{1,200}{100}+\frac{34}{100}$ we can write this number as 12·34.

What is the decimal form of the following fractions?

$\frac{1,064}{100}$ $\frac{1,073}{100}$ $\frac{1,096}{100}$ $\frac{1,106}{100}$ $\frac{1,109}{100}$ $\frac{1,154}{100}$ $\frac{1,196}{100}$ $\frac{1,272}{100}$

$\frac{1,355}{100}$ $\frac{1,429}{100}$ $\frac{1,616}{100}$ $\frac{1,734}{100}$ $\frac{8,168}{100}$ $\frac{1,999}{100}$ $\frac{2,021}{100}$ $\frac{3,056}{100}$

$\frac{4,072}{100}$ $\frac{5,084}{100}$ $\frac{6,088}{100}$ $\frac{7,091}{100}$ $\frac{8,002}{100}$ $\frac{9,008}{100}$

What is the fractional form of the following decimals?

10·11   11·17   12·13   13·09   14·20   17·10   18·41   19·02
27·51   33·15   56·66   77·70   83·33   91·16   96·16   99·99

Operations on hundredths

13.   Since $\frac{1}{10}=\frac{10}{100}$, $\frac{2}{10}=\frac{20}{100}$ ... $\frac{9}{10}=\frac{90}{100}$ we have ·1=·1
·2=·20 ... ·9=·90

We can add $\frac{7}{100}+\frac{5}{100}$ Can we add ·07+ ·05

$\frac{17}{100}+\frac{4}{100}$ ·17+ ·04

$\frac{19}{100}+\frac{15}{100}$ ·19+ ·15

$\frac{6}{100}+\frac{23}{100}$ ·06+ ·23

$\frac{8}{100}+\frac{134}{100}$ ·08+1·34

$\frac{12}{100}+\frac{207}{100}$ ·12+2·07

We can subtract $\frac{24}{100}-\frac{8}{100}$ Can we subtract ·24— ·08

$\frac{73}{100}-\frac{9}{100}$ ·73— ·09

$\frac{87}{100}-\frac{17}{100}$ ·87— ·17

$\frac{135}{100}-\frac{102}{100}$ 1·35—1·02

$\frac{154}{100}-\frac{109}{100}$ 1·54—1·09

$\frac{173}{100}-\frac{153}{100}$ 1·73—1·53

Give the answers to:

·01+·02	·03+·04	·06+·07	·07+·09
·08+·13	·09+·17	·10+·11	·13+·19
·23+·24	·27+·33	·41+·29	·45+·35
·51+·48	·56+·55	·58+·69	·67+·39
·72+·77	·59+·88	·89+·91	·92+·93

Give the answers to:

·03—·01	·06—·04	·07—·05	·08—·07
·09—·04	·08—·02	·06—·01	·09—·08
·13—·09	·14—·07	·17—·02	·19—·09
·24—·06	·24—·12	·36—·23	·35—·24
·39—·27	·40—·20	·45—·30	·46—·43
·47—·38	·52—·44	·55—·53	·56—·50
·62—·52	·64—·59	·67—·66	·68—·67
·77—·73	·85—·82	·89—·83	·99—·97

and check your answers using fractions with denominator 100.

Add ·1+·10   ·2+·10   ·30+·2   ·40+·3

·50+·40   ·1+·2+·3   ·40+·50+·60

·10+·2+·30+·4+·50+·6

Subtract ·4—·30   ·50— ·4   ·60—·3

·5—·20   ·60—·30   ·6—·5

Multiplication of decimals

14. Since we can multiply a fraction by a fraction we know that the product of $\frac{2}{10}\times\frac{3}{10}=\frac{6}{100}$. In decimal notation ·2×·3=·06.

Since the decimal forms of $\frac{12}{10}\times\frac{3}{10}$, $\frac{15}{10}\times\frac{4}{10}$, $\frac{15}{10}\times\frac{12}{10}$ are 1·2×·3 1·5×·4 and 1·5×1·2, and the answers $\frac{36}{100}$ $\frac{60}{100}$ $\frac{180}{100}$, we have 1·2×·3=·36, 1·5×·4=·60, 1·5×1·2=1·80 or 1·8.

Find the answers to:

·3× ·3	·4× ·3	·5× ·4
·6× ·2	·4× ·7	·8× ·5
2·4× ·3	4·1× ·4	1·4× ·5
5·3× ·2	5·7× ·3	6·6× ·4
7·4× ·5	8·2× ·6	9·1× ·3
1·3×1·2	1·4×1·5	1·5×1·5
1·7×1·6	1·8×1·3	1·9×1·2

$2 \cdot 3 \times 1 \cdot 2$ $2 \cdot 4 \times 1 \cdot 6$ $2 \cdot 5 \times 1 \cdot 5$

$2 \cdot 7 \times 2 \cdot 1$ $3 \cdot 2 \times 2 \cdot 2$ $3 \cdot 5 \times 2 \cdot 5$

What do you observe about the way you find your answers?

Check your results using fractions with denominator 10.

15. Since $2 \times \frac{3}{10} = \frac{6}{10} = \cdot 6$, and $3 \times \frac{4}{100} = \frac{12}{100} = \cdot 12$, we can write these multiplications in decimal notation:

$2 \times \cdot 3 = \cdot 6$ $3 \times \cdot 04 = \cdot 12$

Find the answers to:

$3 \times \cdot 3$	$2 \times \cdot 4$	$5 \times \cdot 1$	$4 \times \cdot 2$
$6 \times \cdot 2$	$7 \times \cdot 3$	$8 \times \cdot 4$	$9 \times \cdot 6$
$3 \times \cdot 12$	$5 \times \cdot 11$	$6 \times \cdot 13$	$7 \times \cdot 10$
$9 \times \cdot 20$	$8 \times \cdot 25$	$4 \times \cdot 27$	$2 \times \cdot 51$

Find the answers to:

$30 \times \cdot 3$	$20 \times \cdot 4$	$50 \times \cdot 1$	$40 \times \cdot 2$
$60 \times \cdot 2$	$70 \times \cdot 3$	$80 \times \cdot 4$	$90 \times \cdot 6$

What do you observe if you compare these answers with some of those you have just obtained?

Can you multiply:

$33 \times \cdot 3$	$22 \times \cdot 3$	$55 \times \cdot 1$	$44 \times \cdot 2$
$66 \times \cdot 2$	$77 \times \cdot 4$	$88 \times \cdot 4$	$99 \times \cdot 6$

Can you give a rule for obtaining the answers when we have to multiply either a number by a decimal or two decimals together?

Thousandths

16. If we use one hundred orange rods end to end we obtain a length equal to 1000 white rods. With it we can measure any other length made up of any rods end to end.

For instance $\frac{8}{1,000}$ is the length of the tan rod measured by that length. We shall write the fractions with 1000 as denominator in the following decimal form:

$\frac{8}{1,000}$ will be $\cdot 008$ $\frac{5}{1,000} = \cdot 005$

But since $\frac{80}{1,000}=\frac{8}{100}$ we can write this as ·080 or ·08 and $\frac{83}{1,000}$ as ·083; and since $\frac{800}{1,000}$ is $\frac{80}{100}$ or $\frac{8}{10}$ we can write this as ·800 or ·80 or ·8 and $\frac{830}{1,000}$ as ·830 or ·83.

Now, since $\frac{835}{1,000}$ is $\frac{800}{1,000}+\frac{30}{1,000}+\frac{5}{1,000}$, we can write the decimal form of $\frac{835}{1,000}$ as ·800+·030+·005 and the answer is ·835.

Write the decimal forms of the following fractions:

$\frac{9}{1,000}$ $\frac{2}{1,000}$ $\frac{1}{1,000}$ $\frac{6}{1,000}$ $\frac{7}{1,000}$ $\frac{10}{1,000}$ $\frac{12}{1,000}$ $\frac{15}{1,000}$ $\frac{27}{1,000}$

$\frac{73}{1,000}$ $\frac{97}{1,000}$ $\frac{100}{1,000}$ $\frac{110}{1,000}$ $\frac{115}{1,000}$ $\frac{120}{1,000}$ $\frac{127}{1,000}$ $\frac{200}{1,000}$ $\frac{250}{1,000}$

$\frac{300}{1,000}$ $\frac{301}{1,000}$ $\frac{320}{1,000}$ $\frac{390}{1,000}$ $\frac{399}{1,000}$ $\frac{402}{1,000}$ $\frac{444}{1,000}$ $\frac{500}{1,000}$ $\frac{505}{1,000}$

$\frac{550}{1,000}$ $\frac{555}{1,000}$ $\frac{601}{1,000}$ $\frac{603}{1,000}$ $\frac{690}{1,000}$ $\frac{700}{1,000}$ $\frac{702}{1,000}$ $\frac{757}{1,000}$ $\frac{760}{1,000}$

$\frac{800}{1,000}$ $\frac{810}{1,000}$ $\frac{815}{1,000}$ $\frac{831}{1,000}$ $\frac{900}{1,000}$ $\frac{901}{1,000}$ $\frac{907}{1,000}$ $\frac{970}{1,000}$

Give the fractional forms of the following decimals:

·020 ·002 ·200 2·000 ·006 ·007 ·009 ·13 ·017

·170 1·070 2·001 ·73 ·703 ·730 ·905 ·864 ·85

·9 4·000 5·002 6·012

Operations on thousandths

17. Since we can add and subtract fractions, we can do it on their decimal forms.

Find the answers to the following additions:

| ·813 | ·009 | ·103 | ·111 | ·234 |
| ·115 | ·731 | ·032 | ·889 | ·567 |

| 1·2 | 1·04 | 1·212 | ·003 | 4·013 |
| ·003 | ·107 | ·015 | ·009 | 1·209 |

| 1·006 | ·104 | ·317 | 7·13 | ·451 |
| 2·005 | ·206 | ·683 | ·9 | ·82 |

What do you observe about the way you find your answers?

Check your results using fractions with denominator 1000.

Give the answers to:

1·301	·091	·009	2·205	3·119
−1·2	−·072	−·003	−1·102	−1·992

What do you observe about the way you find your answers?

Check the results by adding your answers to the second term of the subtractions.

Find the answers to the following additions:

·003	·023	1·61	1·701
·307	·105	2·017	2·039
·412	·41	3·4	1·91
·525	·6	1·005	2·010

Check your answers by adding back in the opposite direction.

Multiplication of decimals

18.   We know how to multiply fractions by fractions, so we can multiply those with denominators 10 and 100.

To find the answer to $·2 \times ·03$ we say ·2 is $\frac{2}{10}$ and ·03 is $\frac{3}{100}$; the product is $\frac{6}{1,000}$ which can be written ·006.

Hence $·2 \times ·03$ is ·006.

Find in the same way the answers to:

$·3 \times ·02$	$·4 \times ·03$	$·5 \times ·05$	$·6 \times ·04$
$·7 \times ·06$	$·8 \times ·05$	$·9 \times ·04$	$·9 \times ·06$

and then to the following:

$1·3 \times ·02$	$1·4 \times ·03$	$1·5 \times ·05$	$1·6 \times ·04$
$1·7 \times ·06$	$1·8 \times ·05$	$1·9 \times ·04$	$1·9 \times ·6$

What do you observe in the answers?

Find the answers to:

$1·5 \times ·12$	$1·7 \times ·130$	$1·8 \times ·200$	$1·9 \times ·210$
$2·1 \times ·15$	$2·4 \times ·16$	$2·7 \times ·210$	$3·3 \times ·060$
$4·5 \times ·040$	$5·1 \times ·11$	$5·6 \times ·16$	$6·3 \times ·07$

What do you observe in your answers?

Check by using fractions with denominators 10 or 100.

19. We know how to multiply a fraction by a number. How does it look when we use decimal fractions?

Multiply ·701 by 3. We write the answer first as $\frac{2,103}{1,000}$, which is 2·103. Note that ·701×3=3×·701 since both equal $\frac{2,103}{1,000}$.

Find the answers to:

·621×4	2·101×5	·732×6
9×·312	8×1·215	4×3·145

What do you observe about the way in which your answers are obtained?

Multiply any decimal by 10. What do you observe?

Multiply any decimal by 100. What do you observe?

Multiply any decimal by 1,000. What do you observe?

Can you give a rule for these multiplications, expressed in terms of how many places and in which direction to shift the decimal point?

20. After you have multiplied any number by 10, what must you do to get back to the number with which you started?

After you have multiplied any number by 100, what must you do to get back to the number with which you started?

How does this apply to decimal numbers?

Multiply ·73 by 10 and say what you must do to the answer to get back to ·73.

Repeat this for:

1·15	2·3	4·03	5·52	·012	·009	·102

Multiply ·73 by 100 and say what you must do to the answer to get back to ·73.

Repeat this for:

2·001	·170	·207	3·102	5·012	3·11	6·011	9·315

Can you state, first what would happen if you multiplied these numbers by 1000 and then, what you would have to do to get back to these numbers?

Division of decimals

21. When we go back to the numbers we started with, as we did above, we are dividing the decimals by 10, 100 or 1000.

State it now like this

To divide a decimal by 10 we shift the decimal point . . .

To divide a decimal by 100 we shift the decimal point . . .

To divide a decimal by 1000 we shift the decimal point . . .

and complete the sentences.

Other decimal numbers

22. What we said of fractions with denominators 10, 100, 1000 can be repeated for fractions with denominators equal to 10,000, 100,000, etc.

Fractions like $\frac{2}{10,000}$ or $\frac{31}{100,000}$ can be written in decimal form

$$\frac{2}{10,000} = \cdot 0002 \qquad\qquad \frac{31}{100,000} = \cdot 00031$$

by first writing the numerator; then, starting with the figure on the right, we count the figures to the left and move as many places as there are 0's in the denominator, filling the empty places with 0's.

For $\frac{724}{10,000}$ write 724, move four places to the left starting from 4; there is one empty place left, so put a 0 down; we obtain: $\frac{724}{10,000} = \cdot 0724$. The decimal point is to be put in after the counting of places is finished.

Give the decimal forms of the following fractions:

$$\frac{517}{100,000} \qquad \frac{2,154}{10,000} \qquad \frac{41,021}{100,000} \qquad \frac{27,726}{100,000} \qquad \frac{327}{100,000}$$

If the numerator is larger than the denominator there will be some figures on the left of the decimal point.

51

Just as $\frac{21}{10}=2+\frac{1}{10}=2\cdot1$, so $\frac{215}{100}=2\cdot15$, and $\frac{12,153}{1,000}=12\cdot153$;

likewise we have $\frac{73,421}{10,000}=7\cdot3421$

and $\frac{174,312}{100,000}=1\cdot74312$

Can you give the rule stating where to put the decimal point if you divide a number by 10, 100, 1,000, 10,000, 100,000, etc.?

Does this apply to what you have just been doing?

Observations on the notation

23. Decimal numbers have the same properties as whole numbers if you know where to put the decimal point. Check this statement for all you have done so far concerning

addition of decimals

subtraction of decimals

multiplication of a decimal by a whole number

multiplication of a decimal by a decimal
(with denominator 10 or 100)

Can you now multiply any two decimals? First write them as fractions with denominators 10, 100, 1,000, 10,000, etc.

Find the answers to these multiplications of fractions. Then change the answers into decimals in the way you now know, and see whether your rule about the decimal point is true in these cases.

Which fractions can be written as decimals?

24. Are there fractions other than those with denominator 10, 100, 1,000, etc., which can be written as decimals?

Which are the fractions you know that contain in their family of equivalents one with denominator 10, or 100, etc.?

Which of the following fractions belong to this type of family?

$\frac{1}{3}$ $\frac{2}{8}$ $\frac{1}{2}$ $\frac{3}{4}$ $\frac{7}{8}$ $\frac{3}{7}$ $\frac{1}{8}$ $\frac{2}{25}$

What are the factors of 10? of 100? of 1,000?

Can you always find a fraction equivalent to a given one and with denominator 10, or 100, or 1,000, if the given one has

    a) a denominator that does not contain 2 or 5?

    b) a denominator containing only *powers* of 2 or 5?

    c) a denominator containing multiples of 2 or 5?

$\frac{1}{3}$, $\frac{1}{7}$ are of the first type; find a few others.

$\frac{1}{2}$, $\frac{1}{5}$, $\frac{1}{8}$, $\frac{1}{25}$ are of the second; find a few others.

$\frac{1}{6}$, $\frac{1}{15}$, $\frac{1}{60}$ are of the third; find a few others.

Which, then, can be changed into decimals by first multiplying and then counting of 0's? Show that the examples you have found actually give you decimals.

Recurring decimals

25. In Book 2, Part VII, we considered the procedure for dividing numbers by one another, and we shall now reconsider division for the purpose of finding decimals for all fractions. The writing is complicated but the idea is very simple.

(a) We know that $20 = 6 \times 3 + 2$ and that $\frac{20}{3} = 6 + \frac{2}{3}$. We shall observe this pattern in the steps that follow.

$$\frac{2}{3} = \frac{2 \times 10}{3 \times 10} = \frac{20}{3 \times 10} = \frac{\frac{20}{3}}{10} = \frac{6 + \frac{2}{3}}{10} = \frac{6}{10} + \frac{2}{30}$$

$$\frac{2}{3} = \cdot 6 + \frac{2}{30}$$

$$= \cdot 6 + \frac{\frac{20}{3}}{100}$$

$$= \cdot 6 + \frac{6}{100} + \frac{2}{300}$$

$$= \cdot 6 + \cdot 06 + \frac{\frac{20}{3}}{1000}$$

The pattern is repeated again and again and we see that the next step would yield $\cdot 006$ with a remainder that, in turn, would yield $\cdot 0006$, and so on endlessly.

If we put this as a long division we have:

```
     0·666
    ───────
3 ) 2·0
     20
     20
      2
```

Hence the fraction $\frac{2}{3}$ is an **endless** decimal in which all the figures are 6's.

53

We write $\frac{2}{3} = \cdot 66\dot{6}$, with a dot over the last 6 to express that 6 is repeated. It may be written $\cdot\dot{6}$ and read as **point six recurring.**

(b) To obtain the decimal form of $\frac{2}{7}$ the working is similar but contains more steps. You will need to read carefully.

We know that $20 = 2 \times 7 + 6$ or $\frac{20}{7} = 2 + \frac{6}{7}$

Now $\frac{2}{7} = \frac{2 \times 10}{7 \times 10} = \frac{\frac{20}{7}}{10} = \frac{2 + \frac{6}{7}}{10} = \frac{2}{10} + \frac{6}{70}$

or $\frac{2}{7} = \cdot 2 + \frac{\frac{60}{7}}{100}$

$\frac{2}{7} = \cdot 2 + \frac{8}{100} + \frac{4}{700} = \cdot 2 + \cdot 08 + \frac{\frac{40}{7}}{1000}$

$\frac{2}{7} = \cdot 28 + \frac{5}{1000} + \frac{\frac{50}{7}}{10,000}$

$\frac{2}{7} = \cdot 285 + \frac{7}{10,000} + \frac{\frac{10}{7}}{100,000}$

$\frac{2}{7} = \cdot 2857 + \frac{1}{100,000} + \frac{\frac{30}{7}}{1,000,000}$

$\frac{2}{7} = \cdot 28571 + \frac{4}{1,000,000} + \frac{\frac{20}{7}}{10^7}$

But since $\frac{2}{7}$ is what we started with we shall find the same answers in this order again:

$\frac{2}{7} = \cdot 285714/285714/$ etc. Hence the fraction $\frac{2}{7}$ is an endless decimal in which the figures 285714 in that order repeat themselves indefinitely. This group of 6 figures is called the **period** of the decimal fraction.

If we put this as long division we get:

```
     ·285714
7 ) 2·0
     60
     40
     50
     10
     30
      2
```

When we find a figure met before we know the division will **repeat itself.**

54

(c) $\frac{1}{6}=\frac{1}{2}\times\frac{1}{3}=\frac{\cdot 3\dot 3\dot 3\dot 3}{2}=\cdot 1666\dot 6$

or $\frac{1}{6}=\frac{5}{10}\times\frac{1}{3}=\frac{5}{10}\times\cdot 33\dot 3=\frac{1\cdot 8\dot 6\dot 6}{10}=\cdot 166\dot 6$

or $\frac{1}{6}=\frac{1}{10}\times\frac{10}{6}=\frac{1}{10}\times\frac{1\times 6+4}{6}$
  $=\frac{1}{10}(1+\frac{2}{3})=\frac{1}{10}(1\cdot 666\dot 6)=\cdot 1666\dot 6$

And $\frac{5}{6}=5\times\frac{1}{6}=5\times\cdot 166\dot 6=\cdot 833\dot 3$

or as long division:

$$\begin{array}{r} \cdot 8\dot 3 \\ 6\overline{)\,5\cdot 0} \\ 20 \\ 2 \end{array}$$

It is clear that the long division procedure is the easiest for the changing of any fraction into a decimal.

We must not forget that *these decimals never end*, that is to say, there is *not* a true decimal equal to a fraction of types (a) and (c) in No. 25 above.

Powers of ten; multiplication and division

26. We learnt in Book 2, Part II how to multiply and divide any two numbers. Since we shall now learn to divide and multiply any two powers of ten, we shall be able to work out any multiplication or division of decimals.

$10\times 10=10^2$

$100\times 10=10^2\times 10=10^3$

$1000\times 10=10^3\times 10=10^4$

$100\times 100=10^2\times 10^2=10^4$

Then $\frac{100}{10}=\;\;10$ or $\frac{10^2}{10}=10$

  $\frac{1,000}{10}=\;\;100$ or $\frac{10^3}{10}=10^2$

  $\frac{1,000}{100}=\;\;10$ or $\frac{10^3}{10^2}=10$

$$\frac{10{,}000}{10}=1000 \qquad \text{or} \qquad \frac{10^4}{10}=10^3$$

$$\frac{10{,}000}{100}=100 \qquad \text{or} \qquad \frac{10^4}{10^2}=10^2$$

$$\frac{10{,}000}{1{,}000}=10 \qquad \text{or} \qquad \frac{10^4}{10^3}=10$$

If we write $10=10^1$ can you say in words how powers of 10 combine by multiplication and how they combine by division?

See whether you can answer the following as powers of 10.

100,000 × 100,000   10 × 1,000

1,000 × 1,000 × 1,000

$$\frac{1{,}000{,}000}{100} \qquad \frac{1{,}000}{100{,}000} \qquad \frac{10{,}000{,}000}{10{,}000} \qquad \frac{100{,}000{,}000}{1{,}000{,}000}$$

Application

27. Now multiply

25·3 × 4·2   5·17 × ·25   4·61 × 10·5

first by writing whole numbers and the powers of 10 by which you must divide, and then by multiplying as if there were no decimal points and placing the decimal point in the answers.

Which procedure is the surest and the fastest?

Find the answers to the following divisions

3·65 ÷ 1·50   ·12 ÷ ·32   11·19 ÷ 4·3

first by writing the whole numbers and the powers of 10 by which you must divide, and then by dividing the two numbers as if there were no decimal points and placing a decimal point in the answers. Which procedure is the one you like best?

Make up a few multiplications and a few divisions of decimals.

In most cases of divisions there will be a remainder, since we know that this is the normal case in divisions.

Summary

28. Can you state all the advantages you see in the use of decimals instead of fractions when you are considering:

1) a long series of additions

2) a subtraction of two awkward fractions

You can measure which of the procedures is fastest by the following examples:

$$\tfrac{71}{325}+\tfrac{32}{173}+\tfrac{219}{59} \qquad\qquad \tfrac{1}{13}+\tfrac{1}{15}+\tfrac{1}{17}$$

$$\tfrac{314}{19}-\tfrac{451}{67} \qquad\qquad\qquad \tfrac{2}{73}-\tfrac{2}{111}$$

29. The problem of changing decimals into fractions will be studied in Book 7.

IV

PERCENTAGES

PART IV

PERCENTAGES

A new notation

1. We already know several ways of writing one and the same fraction: $\frac{1}{4}$ is the irreducible fraction of a family of equivalent fractions. It can be written as a decimal, ·25, by dividing 1 by 4 and finding that the division stops after the second decimal, or by multiplying its two terms by 25 and finding $\frac{25}{100}$ as an equivalent fraction which has the decimal form ·25.

What are the fractions you know which have an equivalent whose denominator is 100?

Write down all the forms you know for them.

2. If you consider a fraction with denominator 100, the numerator can be read in a new way, as being so much **per cent**; $\frac{25}{100}$ is also read as 25 per cent and written 25%. This is the way these fractions are read in some practical situations, such as sharing quantities, paying interest, calculating profits and taxes, etc.

In this book we shall only learn to talk of fractions as percentages and of percentages as fractions (decimal or otherwise). In Book 6 we shall use them in practical situations.

We met a few such fractions in No. 1; read them as percentages. All fractions with denominator 10 can be changed into others with denominator 100 and immediately read as percentages

Read:

$\frac{1}{10}$ or ·1 is 10% $\frac{2}{10}$ or ·2 is 20% $\frac{3}{10}$ or ·3 is 30%

Whole numbers can be read as percentages. What are the following?

1 is	%		10 is	%
2 is	%		11 is	%
3 is	%		15 is	%
4 is	%		20 is	%
5 is	%		23 is	%
7 is	%		35 is	%

3. Can you read the following as percentages?

1·1	1·6	3·2
1·2	1·7	4·5
1·3	1·8	5·7
1·4	1·9	6·4
1·5	2·1	8·0

And the following?

·01	·06	3·07
·02	·07	4·06
·03	·08	5·02
·04	·09	7·08
·05	2·04	9·01

4. Now $\frac{1}{1,000}=\frac{\frac{1}{10}}{100}=\frac{\frac{1}{10}}{100}$ is read ·1%

Read as percentages the following:

$$\frac{3}{1,000} \quad \frac{5}{1,000} \quad \frac{9}{1,000} \quad \frac{17}{1,000} \quad \frac{25}{1,000}$$

$$\frac{32}{1,000} \quad \frac{43}{1,000} \quad \frac{56}{1,000} \quad \frac{87}{1,000}$$

The following fractions can also be read as percentages; write down the answers:

$\frac{1}{10,000}=\frac{\frac{1}{100}}{100}=\frac{·01}{100}$ or   %

$\frac{1}{100,000}=\frac{\frac{1}{1,000}}{100}=\frac{·001}{100}$ or   %

$\frac{1}{1,000,000}=$

$\frac{1}{10,000,000}=$

61

5. Start writing any fractions whose denominators are powers of 10 and whose numerators are any numbers.

Read each as a percentage as you did in No. 4.

The various forms of writing a %

6. When you can find a fraction equivalent to a given fraction with denominator 100, reading it as a % is very easy. What happens when such fractions cannot be found?

We know that $\frac{2}{3}$ has no such equivalent fraction. But $\frac{2}{3} = \frac{200}{300} = \frac{\frac{200}{3}}{100}$ and can be read as $\frac{200}{3}$ %.

Either you leave it at that, or you give its decimal form $\frac{200}{3} = 66 \cdot 66$ and $\frac{2}{3}$ is $66 \cdot 66\%$ or $\frac{200}{3}$ %.

Find the percentage forms of the following fractions:

$$\frac{1}{6} \quad \frac{2}{7} \quad \frac{1}{3} \quad \frac{4}{9} \quad \frac{5}{11} \quad \frac{17}{13} \quad \frac{29}{15} \quad \frac{31}{17}$$

7. You have found as many forms of percentages as you have forms of fractions.

Which forms of fractions give a whole number for their % form?

Which forms of fractions give decimals that end for their % forms?

Which fractions give a % form that is:

smaller than 1%

bigger than 1%

bigger than 10%

smaller than 100%

bigger than 100%

Percentages, fractions and decimals

8. If a percentage form of a fraction gives a number between 1 and 10, what can you say of the fraction?

or between 10 and 100, what can you say of the fraction?
or between 100 and 200, what can you say of the fraction?
or between 200 and 500, what can you say of the fraction?

9. Compare the fractions that correspond to
·25% and 2·5% and 25% and 250%
·32% and 3·2% and 32% and 320%
·75% and 7·5% and 75% and 750%
$\frac{1}{4}$ % and $2\frac{1}{2}$ % $\frac{1}{8}$ % and $1\frac{1}{4}$ %
·125% and $\frac{1}{8}$ % ·725% and $\frac{5}{8}$ %
1·25% and $1\frac{1}{4}$ %

10. Which is bigger?

$\frac{1}{2}$ or $\frac{1}{2}$ %	3 or 3 %	10% or 10
$\frac{1}{4}$ or $\frac{1}{4}$ %	$2\frac{1}{2}$ or $2\frac{1}{2}$ %	5% or 5

In the following table we give either the fraction or the % form. Find the other.

F.	%	F.	%	F.	%
	40	$2\frac{1}{2}$		1	
5			50		2
	$2\frac{1}{2}$		75	3	
$7\frac{1}{2}$		$\frac{1}{8}$			4·5
	·2		$\frac{1}{8}$	5·5	
	1·3	·025			$\frac{2}{3}$
75			·125	$\frac{2}{3}$	
40		$\frac{3}{5}$			6·6$\dot{6}$

Applications

11. Since all percentage forms are fractions with denominator 100, we shall have no difficulty in subtracting or multiplying them. 2% added to 5% of the same quantity gives 7%.

If from 12% of something we subtract 9% we get 3%. What is ½ of 25% of something? Or 50% of 25% of that thing?

(Note that when we combine % we must add the words 'of the same quantity' or 'of something', which we did not need to do with fractions because, as we said in No. 2, % only appears in applied arithmetic).

1) I give ⅛ of 2% of something and then ⅕ of 2½%; how much must I give in all?

2) If 30% of 15% of something is 45, how big is that thing?

3) Subtract ⅕ of 40% from ⅓ of 42% of something. What is left?

4) Express as percentages the following:

¼ of ½ of something   ·1 of ·2 of something

5) 1·25 of something is worth ⅔ of something else. How much of the second is worth 100% of the first, and how much of the first is worth 100% of the second?

6) If someone gets 20% of something, and someone else 30%, how much of this thing is left? Express each part as a % of what is left.

7) I get 10% of something and then 9% of what is left and again 8% of what is then left. Which of these parts is the largest?

Can you say what % of what is left is equal to the first part?

8) If I add 10% of anything to it and then take away 11%, how much is left?

64

9) If I had added to something 15% of itself,

or if I had added to it 20% of itself,

or if I had added to it 75% of itself,

what percentage of the new quantity must I take away in each case in order to get back to the original amount?

10) If I know that 14% of something is 2 more than 10% of it, how big is the quantity?

12. Because fractions, compound quantities, decimals and percentages are different forms of the same thing they are often used together in statements. Can you think of such statements?

An example may help you:

If I have to pay 12·5% on $\frac{1}{3}$ of my income, 20% on the next $\frac{2}{5}$ and 45% on the rest, find the percentage of my income which I actually receive when my taxes are paid.

When you have found your statements see whether they are sound and lead to possible operations. The following example shows again what we mean:

If I have to pay as tax 50% on $\frac{1}{2}$ of my income, 100% on the next $\frac{2}{5}$ and 160% on the rest, what is my income? Does it make sense?

CPSIA information can be obtained
at www.ICGtesting.com
Printed in the USA
LVOW13s2217141116
512958LV00011B/75/P